TRINITY
UNITED METHODIST CHURCH
North Port Fl.

Ing Gensemer
Asbury Towers apt 403
Bradenton Florida
Moved to Asbury Towers June 3, 1980

about The author

Frances Avery Faunce born Nov 3, 1888
daughter of Carlos Partridge Faunce and
Sarah Avery (King) Faunce, who were
married Oct 15, 1884 in Salem.

Listed on page 247 of "the Faunce
History and Genealogy" by James Faunce
my first cousin.

I was interested in this book as I
am the daughter of Nellie Faunce Chadwick
The name "Faunce" caught my attention
and I have asked the Church Library
Committee if I can own this book.

See 137

THOSE LATER YEARS

A dear little Book

Those Later Years

FRANCES AVERY FAUNCE

Thomas Y. Crowell Company

ESTABLISHED 1834 NEW YORK

Faunce, Frances Avery.   Those later years.   New York,
    Crowell [1959]   177 p.   22 cm.   I. Title.
    PZ4.F265Th   813.54   59–7666 ‡

TO the memory of my mother
whose gallant approach to later years
is reflected in these pages

TO my father
whose life today at ninety-eight
outruns this book

AND TO my sister
because of whose devotion
they have been free
to live on in our home

Her father died in 1959 according
to The Farence Family History.

CONTENTS

THOSE LATER YEARS

CHAPTER 1

Three Frightened Women

Just by chance Mary Olmstead and I discovered a tie of guilt that suddenly bound us together. Two old school friends of ours were living in The Walden, a rest home some twenty miles away, and neither of us had been to see them.

"I know I should have," Mary said when we met in the supermarket. "They must be lonely."

Of course I had no idea then that in and around her sentence were hidden many problems that men and women face as they grow older—problems to which Mary and I would be giving very special thought in coming weeks.

As I looked at her, I wondered why I hadn't made a point of keeping up our friendship. She had been a serious student in school, yet her dark eyes had laughter in them that made her popular. It was clear now that life had changed that laughter into a more mature look of radiance —the deep-down kind of radiance that has to be won and won hard.

Mary had gone away to do social work, then had married, and a few years ago she and her husband had come back to live in John's old home in our New England suburb. There she had nursed him through a long illness, without time to renew old friendships. After his death, she had spent several months with a niece.

"I've heard about what you went through, Mary," I said quietly.

"Then perhaps you know that I've returned again to stay in our house," she said, pushing her market cart out of the way.

As we talked there in the aisle, I couldn't help admiring her soft hair, marveling that it could stay so ungrayed. My own is white and has been for a long time. Mary Olmstead looked frail, but there was an eagerness in her expression and, I liked to think, a flash of her old-time affection.

"How long have Sue and Janet been in The Walden?" she asked.

"You make me ashamed," I answered, "because I believe they both had to go some time ago."

I'm sure I must have said, "had to go," because that was the way I felt about rest homes then.

I left Mary with thoughts about our friends still nagging at my mind. And, as if to emphasize my sense of guilt at not having gone to see them, the very next day I came across Harriet Barnes waiting by the curb in a parked car. She, too, had been one of our young group, but she and Mary and I had gone three separate ways. In fact, Harriet went out West to teach until she married. Then she seldom came back. Only recently, since her husband's death, had she returned to live with her daughter Eileen's family.

I hadn't seen her for so long that I reached out and shook hands with her quite formally.

"My youngest grandchild," she explained, pointing to the mere baby who was squirming back and forth over the front seat. "I'm quite lame," she went on, "so it's easy to leave me in charge—easy for my daughter, that is."

Harriet frowned with the little old frown she used to have in school and drew her lips firmly together. I couldn't help comparing her with Mary right off. It wasn't just that her hair, which used to be a clear auburn, had become noticeably streaked with gray and white. Those deep blue eyes of hers, which had always seemed on the defensive, were now much less outgoing than Mary's. A warm smile came into them for me, however, and I felt drawn to her, especially in her lively responsibility of the moment.

"I hear that Sue Reinhardt and Janet Coombs are in a rest home," Harriet said. "I'm so sorry for them."

"I know," I said. "They've come back here after a good many years away, as you have. They probably applied a long time ago, because there's quite a waiting list at The Walden."

"I suppose I ought to get to see them," said Harriet, "but Eileen finds it difficult to take me to places where she herself doesn't want to go."

Then I told her about Mary Olmstead and suggested marshaling our forces and going to The Walden in a block.

Over the telephone we three decided that perhaps later we'd make what we called, rather coldly, "a visitation" on Sue and Janet. At first Harriet objected on the plea of her lameness, but I said we could help her around. I didn't know then that Harriet had a sort of pose for raising objections, and that this was just a sample.

Plainly we all shared a desire to become better acquainted with each other, or reacquainted, before we set a definite date to go calling. Over a cup of tea in my apartment we certainly did get to know each other. Almost at once we uncovered a common fear that snapped us together for mutual protection with an almost terrifying tightness. Especially when you consider that at the time we were all enjoying reasonably comfortable lives for women around the seventy mark.

I guess I proved to be the impulsive one of the group, because I started right in by saying, "To tell the truth, I've put off going to see Sue and Janet because I'm frightened, actually frightened, at the thought of having to go to live in a rest home myself, or a boarding home or whatever it may be called."

"I know," agreed Mary with a sudden lack of calmness. "It's a sort of double-barreled fear. First of all, I don't like the idea of not being really *wanted* in my later years . . . by someone . . . somewhere. It seems unbelievable that women like us should have to *apply* for a place to live."

Mary smoothed back her dark hair and then rested her hands quietly in her lap, but I could see that she didn't feel very quiet inside.

The tension lines in Harriet's forehead deepened as Mary said, "You'll probably have to fill in a questionnaire declaring your whole resources—physical, financial, and probably spiritual, too. I've seen those questionnaires," she warned.

Mary went on a little reluctantly, as though she was not used to complaining.

"And in the second place," she said, "I don't know about you, but I'm scared of making the change, whenever the time comes."

As I look back now, I wonder that it didn't occur to Mary, or to Harriet or me either, that these two things—not being wanted and not wanting to go—might be surmounted by prowess, a kind of prowess that could be cultivated in advance. It took time to work that one out. It took time to probe deeply enough for us to recognize that this means prowess of the head, the heart, the soul.

We just weren't seeing clearly. Like many other women of our age, we were undergoing what is called "blind" fear. We shared the feeling that a grim situation was bound sooner or later to run into us head-on, and that it would have to be accepted with set teeth. That first afternoon together, no one said, "But surely we can do something about it; that is, about some of it." We glumly laid our lowest cards on the table and took a sorry look at one another's hands.

Harriet was too independent to let us wait on her. As she limped across the room for her third cup of tea, she said, "I'm not only annoyed at the thought of it. I confess I'm somewhat bitter, and that's no great help. After all, I've lived a good life and now I'm just going to be dumped in a strange place with a lot of other old people; and tell me, what is there left then?"

She looked sour enough without the lemon she was pressing hard with her teaspoon, and she answered her own question: "It's like going into reverse and backing into something you can't see."

I had learned a little about Harriet and couldn't help

understanding her resentment. As a teacher she had been successful and noted for her firm discipline. She had gone on teaching after her marriage until her only child came. Much later, when she was left a widow, she had been able to do some substitute teaching.

"The time soon came," she told us now, "when I felt too lame to command the situation in the classroom."

Harriet had seated herself again in a straight chair because she found it hard to get herself out of an easy chair. She started to cross her knees and set her cup down to lift one leg with both hands, placing it cautiously on the other. You could see that it hurt. Then she began to tell us more about her situation. She had been a welcome enough member of her daughter's household while she was wholly active. She had been a handy baby-sitter when the young couple went out. She had willingly done chores. Indeed, she was glad of them, with her own home broken up.

"I've been careful to keep out of the way in the family life," she made a point of explaining to us. "I love Eileen, of course, and Tom, too. And the two older grandchildren may be rogues, but they are a comfort."

Just when things began to slip Harriet couldn't say. When the third baby was born, Grandma had carried everything while the mother went to the hospital. Perhaps she had advised too much about ways and means of bringing up that baby. And it could be, she admitted, that she was a bit old to be wakened by crying in the night without the power to do anything to stop it. Whatever it was or whenever it began, something had been slipping so that she was no longer a vital, contributing member but a growing care to them all.

Harriet

"No one has had to tell me this," she said. "There are some things you can see for yourself. I can't help feeling that my presence is creating circumstances all too much like the difficulties I saw when my own grandmother was taken into our family. You can't call it friction, exactly. But now the children have to be *sh-sh'd* when I take my nap. There are too many of us using one bathroom. I am the one too many and I know it," Harriet declared. "Besides, as I said, I've become quite lame and I can't do much housework to pay my way."

That was how she put it to us. I was watching Mary's dark eyes and she was watching Harriet. Mary was not smiling, but the outgoing radiance I had noticed that first day had come into her face. I don't know what it did to Harriet, but it gave me a sort of lift that I didn't forget. I felt mighty sure that Mary had something we two didn't have, or didn't have enough of.

"I've told you all this," Harriet then stated, "because it shows what's at the bottom of my reluctance to go over to The Walden to see Janet and Sue. Those two women are in the very fix I'm going to be in. I've got to enter my name on a waiting list somewhere and make the plunge when there's a vacancy. I suppose I could have asked to be driven over there, but I've kept putting it off.

"And that reminds me," she went on. "I must leave promptly when Eileen calls for me on her way from the Cub Scouts, where she's a Den Mother. And then we have to pick up Debbie from dancing class."

We all laughed.

"You see what I mean," she said, and we did.

With Mary the story was quite different. She told us

without complaint about caring for her husband until he had to be hospitalized. That period had seemed only harder. Always the anxiety as to When. Always the feeling of helplessness to help his suffering. Always the tug on the heart and the associations around the house to remind her that he was never coming back.

After he had really gone, she had held herself together for his sake, she called it. She had tried to go ahead the way he would have wished, to throw herself into the interests of others and to eat three good meals every day, without grieving, without "going over things."

"That was an expression of his," Mary said. "He was against regretting the past and always would ask instead, 'Where do we go from here?'"

Mary opened out with astonishing confidence, I thought, and this drew us three very close. She was sitting relaxed, with her ankles crossed easily, but she did make one confession: "I know that those years wore down my physical strength and often seemed to sap my mental and spiritual strength even more. So now there isn't too much left of me."

Harriet leaned forward and said she could understand quite well. Perhaps the sudden going of her own husband had, after all, been the easier way.

"No way is easy," Mary said and there was a remembering look in her brown eyes that did something to me. "The trouble is that I'm not strong enough to keep up the house and I can't get help. No one need tell me that it won't be long before I should go to some Home with a big *H*. I say 'go' because I refuse to wait till I have to be 'put';

and I've told my niece over and over that I shall never live with her, even though she says she wants me. I've been a social worker myself and I know that her job is hard enough. I've seen too often how that kind of arrangement turns out. It looks wonderful at the start for all concerned.

"Yet," she went on, "I can't carry on indefinitely alone, and if I find a spot where I can depend on someone, for a price within my means, I ought to take the step. That's not, however, so simple as it sounds."

We all knew that she was dead right. Then she let herself go and I was glad to know that I wasn't the only one with this dread churning inside.

"You see," she said, "I haven't been over to call on Janet and Sue because I just hate the thought of it so— reducing my possessions to a roomful, leaving my neighbors, rooting myself up from so many things John and I enjoyed together."

"Honestly," put in Harriet, with those tension lines again deepening in her forehead, "I think it's a terrible thing to let yourself in for."

I pushed the tea tray to one side and met them halfway in their restlessness.

"Don't think I find it any less frightening," I admitted. "From things you hear, it seems almost like jumping into a prison camp—regimentation and the food and everything. I wish I didn't feel that way because—because I know I've got to jump, and not too many years from now, as you say."

I stopped and felt the other two thinking, thinking hard. Harriet picked me up.

"But you're fortunate," she said. "You're a writer. You can keep on working. I imagine you'll be writing to your last day. If you can only keep occupied in a place like that, it isn't so bad."

It seemed they both knew that I had been a secretary and then had written textbooks and magazine articles for secretaries. Later I had done children's verse as well. I didn't tell them then about the death, a few years before, of the friend with whom I had shared my apartment for many years. Perhaps they know, I thought, why I now live alone.

But I did say this: "I do hope to have the writing urge for a long time. What really worries me about a rest home is that I won't be allowed to use my typewriter. In fact, the neighbors in the rooms at either side and across the hall 'simply won't have' the sound of that 'awful' typing, and the sound is the very music of my life," I complained.

As I look back, I am glad that the question of being permitted to use a typewriter bothered me, for it showed me at the time that I had a lot to learn about letting go, about giving up my independence.

"I can see it all now," I said, scrunching my shoulders.

But Harriet came back with, "No, that's part of your difficulty. You *can't* see it now. If you're like me, always up to now I've had a chance to select the room or suite of rooms or apartment I wanted to live in. Even Eileen gave me her lovely guest room, the nicest in the house. But with this business, I'll be lucky to have anything whatever *assigned* to me."

"Yes," I agreed, "it isn't just when and where to go. It's whether there's any place at all for you."

I took the tea things out to my kitchenette and, when I came back, plowed on.

"Yet I must admit that some day I shall be truly thankful to have someone to lean on. Since my friend died, I have once or twice known what life feels like when I had to swing out on a rope that no human hands were holding, during an illness. There was no one person to know whether I swung back, whether I still *was* or *wasn't*, although I have many friendly neighbors.

"That's why I'm trying to tune my mind somehow to being thankful later when a place is found with bed and board and a watchful eye over me. I want to welcome this security and be mighty glad of it. But right now I don't seem to know how to feel that way. At least," I continued, "I shan't have to decide, or have someone else decide, whether I might better spend my days with a daughter or daughter-in-law, or a grandson and his family, or any other relative. I haven't any of these on my horizon. So I'm freed from any fear that I might be a so-called 'burden' on the daily lives of my youngers. In this I'm like a host of women, I guess. I don't have any wait-over spot where I belong. No one to say, 'Do come to be with us until . . .'"

My voice must have faltered a little, as I looked down at the floor and added, "And when I do go to a home, I'm not sure that I . . . have . . . what . . . it . . . takes!"

"That's just it," came in Harriet.

"I know," said Mary. Then she added, "You have to have what it takes or go under."

Something in their voices made me want to be strong, strong for myself and even stronger for them. As we paused,

I felt a sort of "deep calling unto deep," and I was strength-
ened myself for having these two comrades. I didn't phrase
it that way to them.

I said, "What a great team we can be! I tell you what
I think, girls (that's what cartoonists like to have us call
each other at our age). I think that, if we can brave it together in one solid phalanx and search into this Thing, we
may get over being terrified. After Easter, let's go to see our
friends at The Walden and face it all down."

Harriet said, oh, she'd seen plenty of rest homes as far
as that went, as if she wanted to evade the whole business,
but Mary looked at her searchingly.

"I'll wager you've never been in one since you knew
Sue and Janet had to go," she pressed. "I haven't."

"I haven't, either," I said and I was ashamed to notice
that my voice sounded on the weak side. It sounded the
way you speak when you're really frightened and are trying to give yourself a dose of courage.

CHAPTER 2

We Look into It

Harriet Barnes was in the car when Mary Olmstead drove to my door on the day set for our "visitation."

"Don't think you can back out now," frowned Harriet. "You started this thing. It's you that's making Mary and unwilling me go to The Walden Home, and don't you forget it."

I knew that she was hiding real fear behind her banter, but as usual I plunged in with chatter of my own.

"Do you know, girls," I said, "believe it or not, I've already chalked up one victory. Remember how worried I was that I wouldn't be allowed to use my typewriter in a rest home? Of all foolish things! I have a fund for extra-specials, and I've already bought a new portable machine that the neighbors in our apartment house say they can't hear. Now I feel all set."

"Anyone would think you were eager to go right now," Harriet said.

"But really," I defended, "perhaps every one of our anxieties could be resolved if we were practical about it."

"That," Harriet countered icily, "is what is commonly called downright optimism."

"But why not be optimistic?" Mary asked.

"Because," Harriet said, "you can't convince me that any number of extra-special funds can buy off the difficulties we lumped together the other day. After all," she went on, turning to me, "you may be practical about your old typing, but that isn't everything by a long shot."

"We might call it a start," suggested Mary. "Perhaps we can shuck off one thing after another, who knows?"

But Harriet wouldn't let go.

"Remember," she reminded us, "The Walden has the name of being a pretty superior place. Don't let yourselves be taken in by it. They aren't all like that, not by any means."

I knew Harriet was right. We were going to visit a home that had a gracious endowment. The main building was originally the residence of a Miss Walden, and her bequest had allowed for generous additions and upkeep. We could feel sure that there would be no lack of cleanliness, no lack of care for our friends, no lack of proper food. It was run on a weekly boarding basis, but many women who had lived there over the years had, out of sheer appreciation, left money to increase the permanent funds.

We had telephoned to Miss Holden, the hostess (I never did like the word "matron"), to make certain that it would be agreeable for us to see Sue Reinhardt and Janet Coombs. She welcomed us with a genial light in her eyes that did not seem turned on just to make an impression.

"I'm going off duty soon and, if you don't mind, I'd

be glad to show you around myself and then leave you
with your friends. They're looking forward to seeing you,"
she said, adding with a gesture, "This at the left is our common living room."

It was furnished, you could tell, with Miss Walden's
family furniture, which gave it a homey look not at all
after the streamlined fashion of today. No chromium. I
could almost see myself sitting cozily here with Mary and
Harriet—and Sue and Janet, of course. It wasn't so bad,
after all, I tried to tell myself.

The dining room looked as though it could seat perhaps fifty people. What struck me first were the transparent
tablecloths with gay patterns showing through the plastic.
I don't happen to like that sort of thing in my own apartment, but I suppose it does save laundry.

Then my eye caught something that almost made me
cry out, first with astonishment and then with a kind of resentment. Across the wide marble mantelpiece stalked two
rows of big cardboard animals. Quacking ducks, oversize
chickens with high-flapping wings, and smug rabbits with
baskets of Easter eggs. All in rather lurid, cheer-up colors.
The huge set-in wall mirror above reflected the duplicate
backs of them all, doubling the procession. I tried to puzzle
this out.

"But surely," I growled to myself, "this isn't a Little
Folks' Home."

I didn't dare look at Harriet, or Mary either, yet I knew
that sometime, sooner or later, those ducks would come
up, would fly up, for discussion—scornful discussion. Miss
Holden waved toward them as she saw our attention glued
there.

"The Guild," was all she said.

The two words were enough. I could seem to hear
the retired social worker in Mary and the teacher in Harriet murmuring, "A Do-Good Project." I didn't know
that later our judgment about the Guild would be softened.

The cook showed us about the tidy, good-smelling
kitchen, with its model equipment recently installed. We
could see that this was really first-rate, and it rather warmed
us after the cold parade of animals.

As we peeked into the orderly office and walked down
the corridor with doors open along the way, the soft hues
of the walls and the personal-looking furniture in the rooms
all pointed to a sort of guest house rather than an institution.
It seemed so ideal as not to be quite real. We all must have
felt that such excellence isn't too common, but it was "easy
on the eyes," as Harriet had promised. And, as Harriet's
lameness made her progress somewhat slow, we had time
to take everything in.

When we came to the long sunroom, we found why
so many of the rooms had been empty of their occupants.
Here the women were sewing in wicker chairs upholstered
with cheerful chintz. Miss Holden began introducing us as a
group, but I noticed that she mentioned each guest by
name. When we were called friends of Sue Reinhardt,
smiles brightened the whole line.

"We're making aprons and other articles," Miss Holden
told us, "for our May Sale, to raise money for The Walden
Club Fund. The ladies vote on what to do with the profits.
Last year, for one thing, we bought the television set you
saw in the living room. But we look out for needy people,
too."

The entire length of the room was strewn with aprons of all sorts, colors, and states of completion. One woman was sitting off in a corner by herself, sewing busily enough. I noticed that she was wearing a hearing aid and I thought, "She's probably having trouble making it work clearly in this buzz of voices."

Miss Holden hastened to explain to us that our two friends didn't work with this group.

"Mrs. Reinhardt," she said, "is doing hooked rugs on a frame in her own room, but of course she joins us in other activities."

I couldn't help wondering what the other activities might be, yet I really wasn't too anxious to find out.

Then Miss Holden went on, about Janet, "And Miss Coombs doesn't seem to care too much for group work. Besides, she almost never leaves her room except for meals— she's so crippled up."

"I haven't seen her for some time," I said, "but I can imagine that Janet wouldn't be too enthusiastic about contributing to a community sale?"

I finished with a question mark and watched Miss Holden's face. It did not commit her in any degree, and I felt that here was quite a person. I wished I could know that every home had a head of such caliber. For the moment, I forgot myself as a possible resident in a place like this. I found my heart going out to the scores of hostesses who are earnestly striving to mold pleasant households out of personal quirks of many shapes and kinds.

Mary, who obviously didn't want to say anything against Janet, remarked somewhat tritely, "I suppose it takes all kinds to make a rest home."

On Harriet's face there was a look of, "For goodness' sake, Mary, don't rub it in. We're seeing a plenty without your pointing that out."

I thought Harriet showed signs of real fatigue and, for that matter, Mary seemed more weary than I had seen her. As we followed our hostess toward our friends' rooms, she let us glance into the well-kept infirmary.

"It looks too good to be true," I said, then went on, "I'm still held by the relaxed faces and peace in that sewing room. Those women don't seem to be merely *resigned* to being here."

Naturally Miss Holden looked pleased, and she said what I had expressed to the girls the week before.

"I think for the most part what you see reflected is the feeling of relief that comes from having someone to lean on. As a caller here the other day said, there comes a time when you can't take a chance of being alone in your house or apartment during some illness, even though your need may be only temporary. You may have friends and neighbors who can run in, but it isn't the same as having someone on call for twenty-four hours a day. That," she said modestly, "may be one key to any satisfaction in their faces."

"You've been very patient with all our questions," said Mary. "I suppose you can see that we belong to the next crop," she added with a rather nervous laugh.

Miss Holden must have noticed that Mary didn't sound enthusiastic, for she gave us an understanding glance and said, "But you girls look young yet."

We didn't answer and she continued, "Looking ahead to it does make an emotional tug on any woman. . . . I wish it didn't," she added as she knocked on a half-open door.

Mary had asked to see Sue Reinhardt first, and there our hostess left us with, "Come often. You'll do our friends good, I know."

Sue was plainly expecting us with real eagerness. She got up out of her chair and, if it hurt her to move, she never winced once. She set her cane to one side and, as she came toward us, seemed to catch us up in her own lightness of heart. She shook hands with Harriet first.

"It's been a long time since you helped write my English compositions," she smiled.

"Do you really remember that?" exclaimed Harriet.

"Before you girls sit down," Sue said, "I want you to see the view from my window."

It didn't seem like much of a view to me, compared to what I see from my apartment, but I didn't say so.

Mary held out a bunch of spring flowers.

"We brought these for your room," she said.

Sue took them in her hand and sniffed their sharp fragrance.

"Do you know what?" she asked. "One of the guests here is missing the jonquils in her old home garden. And you've brought me so many!"

Mary sat down on the edge of the day bed with a gesture of mock despair.

"Just keep some for yourself, Sue, that's all we ask!" she laughed.

Harriet took the straight chair by the window and I went to find a vase. As I came back, Mary was fingering the brass handles on an old mahogany desk.

"This looks like an heirloom," she remarked.

"Yes," Sue said, "it was my mother's. By writing little notes there I find I can keep in touch with old friends, but I must say I'd rather see them. It's good of you to come."

Mary had arranged her flowers on the table.

"You can begin giving them away after we're out of sight," she teased, then went on: "That low blue vase on your shelf is beautiful. It's Venetian glass, isn't it?"

"Yes," replied Sue, "it's one of many pieces we had in our home. Down in Kentucky that was. My friends knew that I was making a collection and often brought me precious bits as hostess gifts."

I had heard that Sue lived in considerable affluence, entertaining with Southern ease until her husband died. Then she discovered that most of their eggs had been invested in one basket—a basket full of holes.

"I let my young people have the rest of the glass collection," she continued. "There's no point in storing things you're never going to use again yourself. The new generation might as well enjoy them now as to wait. But I did bring that one favorite here to The Walden."

I don't know how it seemed to the others at the time but Sue sort of "got" me. She was so even-voiced, without being pious. She looked so honest-to-goodness good. I remembered then that in school she never used to get ruffled the way some of the rest of us did.

"After all," I thought to myself, "it pays out."

"You'll come again, won't you?" Sue urged, when we started to leave her.

We all said, "Thanks, Sue," but I noticed that no one made any promises. I found my thoughts whirling in a sharply cut circle, and I—a future I—was in the center of that circle.

"Janet's room is two doors up the hall," Sue said. "I won't go with you because I think she might like to see you by herself."

I wondered what Sue meant. Someone had warned us about Janet Coombs, and Mary and I were glad to hang back at Harriet's pace. Janet pointed to her two canes and didn't rise. As I expected, she greeted us with a honeyed smile.

"Simply marvelous to see you . . . such a treat . . . so darling of you to come!"

I watched her burble and was ashamed to suspect her sincerity.

"Janet Coombs," I'd been told, "is just the way she used to be—sugar sweet, but with a 'kicker' all ready for you."

It seemed mean to watch for it, but the first kicker wasn't long in coming.

She began with, "I said to myself before you came that you would go to see Sue Reinhardt before you got in to see me, and I was so very glad, very glad."

Then the stinger poked out in the very tone of her voice as she asked, "You did, didn't you?"

I said in a matter-of-fact way that Miss Holden happened to take us there first.

Janet gave me a look that argued, "She would!" but what she really said was, "Let me see, her room doesn't come first, but of course it doesn't matter, does it?"

Nobody answered that one, so she went on entertaining us, in her way.

"Well anyhow, I'm always the one to wait and I suppose it's a good thing that I've got so much patience. Sue isn't wealthy any longer," she ran on, "as perhaps you know. But I guess we all end in the same boat, no matter what we have."

Again no one spoke, so she went on, "I am so sorry, very sorry to see you with that cane, Harriet. Who would ever have thought of us two . . . you know what I mean . . . basketball and everything! The doctor actually tells me to move about." She pretended a bright smile here, then continued, "But that's for him to say. You know doctors."

Harriet held out her bouquet this time and Janet looked it over as if to ask, "These can't be for *me?* Nobody ever brings *me* anything."

She made a rather hollow bow. I can't for the life of me tell what made it look so hollow. Then she came out with a gush of thanks: "My favorites . . . such a golden hue . . . how lovely of you, very, very lovely . . ." With my eyes on the blossoms, I forgot to be on guard for the kicker. But it came: "Well, I do like having flowers," she remarked, almost drawing back from them, "only 'They' never can get the right kind of container here. I sometimes think 'They' don't have any imagination at all."

I wanted to say that perhaps it was vases "They" didn't have, but I kept still.

"Of course," and she was quick to turn on that smile again, "of course, I never have any complaints to offer."

Mary picked up a magazine from the bedside stand and turned the amusing cover toward Janet.

"Oh, that!" exclaimed Janet. "By the time magazines get given to me, they're so old I might as well not have them."

Then Harriet took over.

"It seems so restful and quiet here," she tried, doubt-less thinking of Eileen's household.

" 'Quiet'?" repeated Janet with a twist of her face. "You wouldn't think so if you had that bathroom right next to you. I don't know why they can't fix those pipes. They don't half try, that's what I say."

"You have a lovely old Chippendale desk," I threw in with perhaps not too friendly a tone. "It looks as though you'd brought it from home," I added, remembering Sue's.

"Don't say 'home' to me," Janet snapped back and I thought of how innocent a turtle can look. "They call *this* a home. That's my desk all right, but the room's so small it takes up the whole place. I can't write at it any more because I have to move this heavy chair out of the way every time. But then, I don't have anyone much to write to. I don't know how that Sue Reinhardt manages to get so much mail. Everybody talks about it. As for me, I just don't look for letters any more."

Then she gave a sigh, the kind that seems planned.

"I keep asking," she said, "why this had to happen to me . . . of all people. You three are lucky. Sue and I just got hit first, that's all."

Harriet's endurance must have been near an end be-cause she murmured half under her breath to me, "It really isn't what you have but what you are."

I determined to remember that sentence. It had every-thing in it. But Janet didn't pay any attention, even if she did hear.

She just went ahead with: "That Sue makes me more than mad because she keeps saying she likes it here. And besides, she isn't nearly as ailing or anything as I am. Not many of the inmates are."

I recalled that Sue had used the word "guests." I know it wasn't too kind of me but I thought, "Janet seems rather like an 'inmate' herself. This place is no more than a prison to her."

We started to leave and Janet fell all over us with sugared words. I decided not to decide whether she meant them. It was good that we had to go out through the sun-room again, where the "ladies," as they had been called, nodded brightly to us over their sewing. I couldn't help believing that as a whole they were an agreeable lot, and I said so as we walked down the driveway to the car.

"Maybe so," remarked Harriet, "but you couldn't see how they really feel about it all . . . way inside, I mean."

CHAPTER 3

On the Way Home

Because the day had been unseasonably warm for April, I had ridden in the back seat on our way over to The Walden. But when we got into Mary's car now, she said, "Why don't you sit in front with us? There's plenty of room."

This told me more than anything she could have said. Mary, I thought, feels that we have reason to stick closely together, that we need the security of our threesome. My mind flashed back to that infirmary. The neatness and the whiteness of it. The patients obviously well cared for. I knew that this was pleasant to remember but I knew also that fear had somehow "gat hold" of me anew, and I couldn't help wondering about Harriet. She was dead quiet except when she forced a remark about a bed of crocuses we passed, beside a low white fence.

"Maybe Harriet is taking the right tack," I said to myself. "We can put off even thinking about this thing for ourselves till the event is thrust on us."

I suggested this to my companions, and my cowardice must have stuck out clearly.

Harriet said, "Of course. We might be killed in an accident and all our worry for nothing."

"Thanks for that," said Mary, with her eye on the road. We all managed a laugh, but it was pretty empty.

"I think it's really as Janet stated," I said coldly. "We all seem heading for the same boat and, at that, the boat we three board may not be half so nice as The Walden."

I somehow felt that all of us had changed in that short, sobering hour. We had come face to face with reality, a very personal reality. And, individually or together, we didn't like it.

"Do you know," I went on, "our visit reminds me of the college freshman whose mother left him at the door of his dormitory on the opening day. He was a normally devoted and affectionate son, by the way.

"His mother asked eagerly, 'Aren't you going to kiss me good-by, Bob?'

"He hesitated, and she urged him with, 'That freshman over there is kissing his mother.'

"And Bob came back with a stern 'You see how it looks!'

"That," I concluded, "is the trouble with us. We've seen how it looks." Then I went on with mock cheerfulness, "You might say that you can find a lot that's good about it—about The Walden, I mean. Besides, over the years, I've known any number of women who have kept contented or at least reasonably contented right up to the last."

"But were those women in rest homes?" probed Harriet, with light sarcasm in her voice.

"Well, no, not all," I admitted reluctantly, trying to hold to my point. "How about you, Harriet?" I asked, laying a friendly hand on hers to show that I was really with her. "Do you always knock holes in other people's ideas?"

"Oh, I suppose so," she answered. "You have to be realistic. I'm free to admit that the mass production of those aprons made me feel sort of sick. Not that they were all alike, but they seemed part of a hopeless routine. I hate to sew. In fact, I don't know how, and it looks as though you'd have to want to sew. The only things I can do with my hands are to cook and garden, and you can see where that's going to leave me in a place like The Walden."

"There must be other things you could make in the Busy Hour," offered Mary a bit wryly. "What about leather belts?"

We answered her with a groan because we knew that she meant any made-up busy-ness, and we resented the idea of being directed.

"If you want to know what got me," I said, giving in to Harriet's honest mood readily enough, "it was that row of white heads in the sunroom. That stock hairdo! Every one of those heads done like every other, along that whole line, like the cap of a uniform. It was as if the same shepherd had shorn the entire flock and his wife had given a Walden Permanent. Their faces did attract me, but those spring permanents made the women look as impersonal, or unpersonal, as ever a set of human beings could."

I knew Mary and Harriet were aware that I wasn't ridiculing the "ladies." I was merely stunned by the pos-

sibility of ever having to give in to such a pattern. Perhaps
I did pride myself on a simple style for my hair which, to
be sure, was every bit as white as theirs.

I felt of my own plain bun now and said, "That's what
I don't believe I'd like."

"You haven't asked me for my gripe," put in Mary,
and I was glad to have her speak out because I'd been harboring a feeling that Mary was going to be much too good
for Harriet and me. "That awful decorated mantelpiece in
the dining room, with the Easter parade. You know—the
rabbits and the ducks, provided by the Guild."

"You mean," corrected Harriet, "the bunnies and the
duckies," and we all did smile.

After this we didn't talk much, not until Mary drew up
at my door. Then she said, "There's one thing. Sue Reinhardt has what it takes."

"And she always will," asserted Harriet.

"Exactly what do you mean by that, girls?" I demanded
and I saw Mary start to answer. "You'd better turn off your
engine," I suggested.

"Well, what struck me about Sue was her buoyancy,"
she explained. "It didn't seem put on. She has a resilience
that lets her spring back quickly from a touch of pain, if
you noticed, or from some reference that might deaden
conversation."

Harriet drew a quick breath.

"I'll tell you what Sue's like," she said. "She's like a
rubber band that snaps back into shape. She really stays
Sue, not because she's rigid, but because she's elastic."

"You're right," said Mary.

As I saw her start to turn on the ignition, I knew that I didn't want them to go.

"Can't you two come here to my apartment a week from today?" I urged. "Not just to pick up with each other again, but to face this thing together."

"If we can really bring our fears out into the open," said Harriet firmly. "It's all well and good for us to fuss about rabbits and ducks, about uniform hairdos, and making aprons, but you both know as well as I do that there's a lot more to it than that."

"Of course," I agreed.

"We might best call spades spades," Harriet went on. "For example, who wants to be herded with other people whose infirmities are more than catching up with them, when you know you're going the same way? You don't have to be told what I mean, Mary. You haven't been a social worker for nothing."

Harriet didn't wait for Mary to speak.

"Either," she continued, "they get crotchety because they can't hear or they mind noises, like Janet, because they hear too well. They get morose because the world isn't what it used to be. Their hands are shaky so they spill their food."

Here Mary interrupted. "Aren't you mixing up things, Harriet?" she asked. "There are failings you can avoid, or try to avoid, but some of them simply have to be accepted. Shaky hands just are shaky, that's all, whether they belong to you or to someone else. And some people find eating difficult because they don't see so well any longer. Or there's this: if you have a little dry tickle or cough that bothers people around you, you may be able to control it somewhat, but such dryness often comes with aging. If it comes, it comes."

We seemed to be getting into rather depressing details so I tried a lighter turn.

"You are saying, then, that besides this business of having what it takes, you have to *take* what you *have?*" I inquired.

Harriet started to smile but she would push on.

"I told you I'd been to plenty of homes," she said. "I've known many elderly people and what worries them. They like to complain of real and imagined symptoms. I suppose it's trite to say so."

"It may be trite," I said, "but that's something that often begins long before old age."

"Then there's the matter of food," Harriet went on. "If you've been a good cook yourself, it's something to have to sit down day after day and be served things you've never liked to eat or don't like cooked that way. You see other people glancing at their plates and then comparing what has been allotted to your plate. If you have a tray brought to your room for protection from some of this, you are bound to be lonely. If you don't, you may be seated at table with those you can't get used to."

I dared to interrupt with a contrary touch.

"And who probably can't get used to you," I put in.

"Then it's partly the way people chatter," pursued Harriet, fingering her cane. "I always hate getting caught with someone who runs on and on, is likely to be full of malicious gossip, and insists on telling the same old remi-

niscences over and over and over. I think I can stand seeing physical failing better than mental slipping anyway.
And I don't know whether it's worse to become confused
yourself or to see someone else that way."

Then Mary broke in with the little uptilt of her thinking that I had noticed before. "I can't imagine that *all* these
things will happen to you or to anyone else." She paused.
"Any more to get out of your system, Harriet?" she asked,
and I saw her reason.

"If you really mean that," Harriet said, "I'm downright
realistic about a lot of things you come up against—things
you don't like and can't change, in yourself or anyone else.
To come straight down to it, nature brings along a lot of
unpleasant difficulties with old age—things that people
can't help, but they talk about them. You know what I
mean."

We didn't try to argue with Harriet and she continued.

"Don't let yourself think, either," she said, "that the
chatty woman is necessarily the worst. I've known women
so glumly silent at table that you wish to goodness they
would say what they're thinking—that is, if they *are* thinking. Sometimes they'll keep still simply to show that they
don't approve of what you've just said or done—a sort of
pious reproof that you can't quite pin on them because
there's nothing to quote."

"Oh, Harriet," I said, "your picture gets worse and
worse!"

"Sorry. It's nothing but the truth," she defended. "I
know about it all, from hearsay and from plenty of on-the-
scene witnessing of my own. Wherever I boarded when I

was teaching, there always seemed to be these older people. I liked them but I saw how they were. For myself, I just hate to get into it for good and all."

"You seem to mean for bad and all," I said.

"Let's not struggle too hard," suggested Mary. "There's that old saying, 'Easy does it.'"

Harriet and I didn't speak and Mary went on.

"You know how it is with your bulbs," she said. "Your bed of jonquils and narcissus blossoms and hyacinths is ripe with color and vigor. You sniff the strength of spring because it is the 'prime of life' for them. But see what time makes happen to those blossoms—the story of all life. Symptoms of fading creep in to mar your garden. The leaves yellow and droop. And what's happening? The answer is commonplace. And yet, is it? The very character of the flower and leaves is storing itself in readiness for the return of another spring."

Harriet sighed. "I know it, Mary. I know what you're thinking. But isn't all that too idealistic—for us, that is?" Then she went on: "Besides, those other people batten upon your sympathy and even wear you down."

Of all women, I thought, Mary knew what it was to be worn down, and she had an answer.

"Perhaps some of that wearing down has to be," she admitted. "But I have a feeling that naming over these disagreeable facts as such, right here in this car, is going to be a help to us in taking them when or if they come. It's the unnamed fear, the fear that you don't dare to breathe to anyone, that really gripes the hardest."

"I must say," I put in, "that Harriet has gone graphic enough to save us from being called ostriches."

"And now I wish I could forget it all," Harriet sighed, "that is, until the time comes when I positively have to join the Sues and the Janets—which is soon enough, dear knows."

"Let's not try to forget it; let's get ready for it," Mary said crisply. "We've faced this thing now. You know how it is when there's a noise in the night. You ask through the dark, 'Is someone there?' Then you turn on your flashlight and find it was your wicker chair squeaking. You say, 'When I saw what it was, I settled down.' "

But Harriet would have the last word.

"Yes, and no, Mary," she said. "With the wicker chair you stop your fear because it is, indeed, nothing. But this . . . this thing . . . we have to admit *this* is *something!*"

CHAPTER 4

We Three Keep at It

As I unlocked my door and stepped into my apartment, it seemed the most wonderful haven in the whole world. Perhaps it was the very independence of it. Everything here was mine. Here I was free. The contrast to what we had just seen startled me, and I stared straight into my hall mirror.

"Well," I demanded, searching my face, "do you have what it takes?"

I was not too hopeful. For days, around my rooms, I found myself fighting against ever having to make this threatening change.

The next week, when Mary and Harriet came, they wore a serious air—a kind of cover-up seriousness, I thought.

"They've been at work on their own battlefields," I observed to myself.

"Here's the rest of the Planning Board," announced Harriet, and as usual I jumped right in.

"I have a quotation for you, for us, from *Twelfth Night*. You both know it, where Olivia says, 'There lies your way, due west.' And Viola replies, 'Then westward-ho! Grace and good disposition attend your ladyship.'"

Harriet let herself down into a chair.

"Our way lies due west all right," she said, "toward the setting of the sun."

I could tell that she hadn't really accepted the idea yet.

"So according to Shakespeare, it's Rest Home, ho!" she added.

This touch made us laugh, but then Mary struck an earnest note.

"That 'grace and good disposition attend your ladyship' ought to take care of those sordid details Harriet insisted on laying before us the other day," she said.

"I suppose you are urging us to lay in a stock of good disposition?" Harriet asked.

"Grace and good disposition are what Sue Reinhardt has now," answered Mary, "however she may have come by them."

"And what friend Janet Coombs hasn't," commented Harriet. "I may be disagreeable in my own way but I promise not to throw barbs from behind a bland smile, like Janet. But there," she chided herself, "that's a barb of another kind."

I wanted to start discussing some of our apprehensions and turned to Mary, who had taken out her knitting.

"Do you remember that first day," I asked, "you said

it seemed unbelievable that women like us should have to *apply* for a place to live? That we shouldn't be really *craved* by someone?"

Harriet interrupted.

"I know exactly what Mary meant. As you grow older," she said, "it's a stinging blow to find yourself not wanted, or to find, as I have, that you're taken into a younger family but really welcomed only under their sense of duty."

"That sting isn't confined to old age," remarked Mary. "Anyone may get frustrated by it. The wallflower is invited to a party where she isn't wanted, and she knows it. 'No one asked me to dance,' is her dull report at home."

Mary, the social worker, giving a case, I thought, and she went on.

"Or take the boy who's good in school and may be spoken to by the neighborhood gang, but isn't included in their secret maneuvers. He cries out to his mother, 'I just don't belong.'"

"That hurts at any age," I agreed, "but especially when you are older and feel strength slipping so that you can't run outdoors or scrub a floor to work the hurt off."

"The thing that peeves me is that I have always been wanted," claimed Harriet, "or felt that I was, wherever I lived. I am really the same person I always was, and I'm bound to be Harriet Barnes right to the end."

Her cane slipped to the floor, but she motioned that she would get it for herself.

"Yes," I said, "I'm coming to the place where my strength falls short of independent living, but I'm still going to be I."

I made a gesture toward Mary, hoping for some solution to what Harriet and I were trying to say.

She waited, then said slowly, "I think that is rather a good thing. The fact that you're going to continue to be you means that you have the power to continue to make yourself a home wherever you are and under whatever circumstances. That is, if you have a home within yourself, you'll never truly lack, no matter what the shortcomings or the restrictions of your living-place."

I felt myself relaxing a bit.

"With that way of thinking, if you have this grace-and-good-disposition business ready," I said, "perhaps you don't need to be worried about those later years. I suppose you might be very much liked somewhere . . . even . . . even if you had to go to a county hospital or a state home. Not," I added, "that those places would be by any means like The Walden."

Mary asked me to hold a skein of yarn for her to wind and I moved a chair opposite her.

"I've decided," she said, "that what you need most you can have after all. You need to be an all-round livable person. If you have stamina that others can count on, you can count on it yourself."

Harriet agreed in her realistic way.

"You mean," she phrased it, "that home is a kind of store we keep inside ourselves. What we buy and sell there is, well, is what we buy and sell right there."

"Then let's stop worrying about not being wanted," I said. "But what about that other point of Mary's—of not wanting to make a change? I've been thinking a lot about that. It isn't just the common 'inertia to change.' It's something more."

"That's right," said Harriet. "When I ought to go, and maybe that's mighty soon, I don't want to be filled with dread. I want to *want* to go, impossible as that sounds."

"You've named the very thing we're after," Mary approved, winding her ball of yarn evenly. "We need to prepare ourselves to want to want to go, or at least to be willing to be willing to go. I'm speaking for myself. It looks as though I ought to give myself a good-natured shake-up to see where I stand. If I have a sort of workout, I may be able to snuff out my fears and ease myself into a promising forward swing.

"I've been thinking about this question of change," she went on. "So many of the pleasing things of life do involve getting used to change, and this requires adaptability, a sort of giving-in-ness, and considerable courage. Just look at the struggle of the little child who shifts from creeping and pushing himself around on the floor to the trial position of standing upright. See the new point of view that must be accepted at this new level. But see, too, the sense of achievement, the fresh possibilities for getting into mischief," here Mary smiled, "and the triumph not only of walking but eventually of even running."

"Yes, I've been watching our little Tommy do that," said Harriet. "And here's another illustration of your point. I've seen it so often on the first day of school. Strange new companions sitting all around the new pupil, and a teacher that has to be shared instead of an all-giving mother. Yet, in spite of being scared and even resisting," she went on, "children do come quickly to love a lot of things about going to school."

Harriet drew herself up as though she felt herself yielding and intended to be on guard against this giving-in business.

"I suppose, Mary, you think we'll come to love a lot of things about going to a rest home?" she asked, as if to turn around and eat her own words.

Mary ignored this and continued. "Of course, it goes on long after that, this necessity for changing. The day of leaving home for further education or work, with unknown adjustments ahead in a strange environment. Almost everyone has known homesickness. Then there comes marriage, perhaps. The first baby, with what changes in household routine! The move to a distant city because of some business or professional call, with the leaving of friends and associations. The first child marries. The first member of the family dies.

"Every move," Mary went on, "makes a big difference and we have to adjust to those differences if we want contentment. Instead of clinging to the familiar and the comfortable in our past, we have to settle comfortably into the present. I know," she confessed, "that this is the kind of security I need to get set for. I hope it isn't fantastic to believe that there's always a chance for my growth, even after I do have to give up my own home.

"This all reminds me of my old professor-friend," she said, as I swung the last of her skein from side to side. "One day when she was in the early nineties she spoke wistfully of wishing that she might be at certain meetings at a lake resort which she used to attend. But then she reproved herself swiftly. With a flourish of one hand toward her walls, which were lined with books, she snapped herself out of it with, 'What am I saying? Why, just in this one room, I have more than enough to grow on.' Growing at ninety! And you could always count on her for this pleasant shift of attitude. She could change in a flash."

Mary must have seen that Harriet and I were interested, for she went on, "One day on the street, for instance, a question was asked about her health, which had not been good. She started to answer, then straightened her bent figure on her stout staff and looked up and away. Her reply was as vigorous as it was evasive.

" 'See,' she exclaimed, 'those two pine trees against the blue! What a reach of sky!'

"This wasn't a pose. She simply had schooled herself to look merrily up to see pine trees while others might be looking grimly down at weeds. She had cultivated a habit of keeping her attention on the affirmative. And in her reading and thinking she followed schools of affirmative thought and expectant prayer.

"Nothing," Mary told us, "seemed shut out of her life except the negative. I never went to see her without coming away stimulated. I didn't have to plan subjects to talk about because her interest was flagging. She entertained me, and not with her physical ailments, unless with some droll touch. Beside her was a small scrapbook of clippings she was forever gathering—all humorous. The latest entries she would read aloud, even with the dimmed sight of one eye and with a chin that quivered from weakness. . . . Shall I go on?"

"Do," Harriet and I urged.

"A friend brought to her a beautiful great portfolio from Italy, with loose-leaf reproductions of the works of the masters of the Old World. Many of these my professor had seen in the original in one or another church or gallery abroad. She and I went over these at leisure, setting one at a time in front of us, and she would make comment on what her sharp mind saw—a cloud, a lace cuff, a touch of gold. The world of art was one of her worlds.

"Or she had a booklet to lend, giving a lively treatment of international peace or it might be of personal peace. The books on the table within her reach (it was difficult for her to rise from her chair) were old and new—travel, science, art, philosophy, biography, religion, poetry. Often she insisted on my taking home her most recent copy of the *Reader's Digest*. With the air of giving me assignments as she had years ago in the classroom, she told me to read everything she had checked in the contents listed on the cover. And when I reached home, I found that the breadth of her interests led her to make equally black and insistent checkmarks against almost every item in the issue!

"Her concern for people stayed broad, too. Day in and day out, she wrote a sheaf of letters to former students and friends—in uncertain penmanship, but steady in her ideas. Even at ninety-three she was going strong.

"And here is something else," Mary added. "Although I lived only a few doors away from her, if she heard that I was ill, she would mail an envelope to me. The note was always a gem, with sparkling facets of understanding, of affection, of mirth, of wonder at something in the great world outside petty concerns. As she said about her library, she gave *me* 'enough to grow on.'"

Harriet made a gesture of half-unbelief in this story.

"Was she really in reasonably good health?" she asked.

"She had to stump along with a leg tightly bound and she had gnarled hands and no sight in one eye," Mary answered. "But she made do with the faculties she had in a spirit of fortitude spiced with occasional roguery."

"Weren't her mental processes slipping at all?" Harriet insisted.

"Whenever her memory tried to play her false," Mary explained, "she made a motion like brushing off a fly, as if she would have none of that kind of doings. And she would either call the forgotten thing into play or overlook it and slide into some other idea. With her it was a game to defy the fact of waning powers."

Then I spoke, rather slowly.

"I can't help being convinced that, even with the fading of a mind, the former set of the sails makes a difference. Her soul wasn't waning, if that isn't too pious to say."

Harriet looked past me at Mary, with one more challenge.

"But your professor wasn't in a rest home, was she?" she probed.

"You're right there, Harriet," Mary replied. "She wasn't. And I know what you mean. In her roomy apartment she had with her one of those rare people, a combination companion-nurse-housekeeper-cook. Even if I could find such a person for myself, I couldn't afford it."

"And I wouldn't have room in my apartment for another person," I said.

Harriet made a gesture of despair.

"And for me? It would drive Eileen's family wild to have not only Grandma, but someone to take care of Grandma," she said. "That would be exactly two too many. Your professor, I take it, had everything pretty much her own way in her living."

"That may be, and perhaps she did have a strong will,"

Mary admitted. "I don't know whether she could have given in gracefully to life in a rest home, even one as nice as The Walden. And yet she might have, and at the present moment I wouldn't dare state that much about myself."

"You might or you might not?" came in Harriet.

"I've been thinking about the wide difference between being in control of a regime of your own," Mary said, "and being a part of a community with its fixed routine. But an institution has to be an institution, even though it may at the same time have a heart. There must be a technique for what you call fitting in."

I stepped to the window to lower a Venetian blind and commented, "Without being willful on the one hand or too meek on the other, I suppose. I've been thinking about this very thing and yesterday at my typewriter I started to fool with the wording of the original Declaration of Independence, with us in mind. Perhaps this is part of what Mary means by a 'technique,' " I explained, taking a paper from my desk. "I picked a few sentences and phrases from the familiar Declaration and put them together for our purpose, something like this:

MY DECLARATION OF DEPENDENCE

When, in the course of human events, it is necessary for me, as an aging person, to give up the separate and free way of life to which the laws of my younger nature and of nature's God entitled me, and to join one of the protected bands of elderly citizens, the causes of my Declaration of Dependence will be self-evident.

I believe that in this new form of living the rights of life, liberty, and the pursuit of happiness will be justly regulated. I believe that all members will be held to be created equal in a way most likely to effect the safety and comfort of all. I believe that rules should not be changed (for my sake, that is) for light and transient causes. And I believe that I should be well-disposed and patient for the guarding of my future security.

I intend to conform to rules that are the most wholesome and needful for the welfare of all and not to resent firmness toward my thoughtless invasions on the rights of other people, albeit with a right to appeal to the fairness of the governing.

In all this I appeal to the Supreme Judge of the world for the rightness of my intentions and willingly declare that I am, and of right ought now to be, Dependent, and that I have full power to do only such acts and things as dependent persons may reasonably do. And for the support of this declaration, with a firm reliance on the protection of Divine Providence, I pledge to cooperate with my life and my sacred honor.

Mary and Harriet sat thinking. None of us knew then that I had chanced to leap ahead to specific topics that we three would be threshing out, sometimes by ourselves but often with the help of Sue Reinhardt.

"You make me see, for one thing," said Harriet, "that I've got to get myself used to the idea of giving in more. I suppose Eileen gives in to me more than I like to admit."

"That's it, Harriet," said Mary. "It doesn't mean giving up, just giving in with a good grace. We aren't going to give up our individuality. We shall keep it, but with a difference."

"In other words," I said, "if you want someone to depend on, you've got to give them leeway with you, within their own capabilities and their own judgment. Right now this seems a high price to pay for having someone to call on in need. Yet, when you look way ahead, it really is a relief to picture someone you have a right to look to without any sense of imposing. And I must say that there will come a time when I shall enjoy meals prepared without my planning, shopping, or cooking. I shall really be exchanging freedoms for welcome benefits. But believe me, at present I certainly do like my independence. In fact, I like it very much."

I felt Harriet yielding a bit more.

"I suppose," she confessed, "because I've been a teacher and responsible for discipline, I hate to think of being under any discipline myself. I'll have to follow rules in some home."

Mary came in on that note.

"You probably have to follow rules now in Eileen's house?" she suggested.

"Grandma's set times for using—and not using—the bathroom!" groaned Harriet.

"And I have to follow rules in my apartment house," I put in. "But that's group life for you anywhere. I made extra copies of my Declaration of Dependence for you girls," I added.

"Thanks," said Mary. Then she said slowly, "Somehow

you make me wish that, when my baggage has to go through some unknown doorway, I may hold my head up and make a gallant approach to the new life. Let's picture ourselves that way. I must say I hope to be the kind of elder statesman that could sign this declaration and then graciously abide by it."

When they had gone, I turned to the hall mirror once more to search my face. I believed I saw a little less fear. But when I went into my convenient kitchenette to get dinner, something seemed to creep over me again. I fixed one of my pretty company salads, the sort I don't usually bother about just for myself, and I loved being able to go ahead without asking anyone's say-so.

I took a tray out to my tiny porch. It didn't seem so tiny after all, not now. I felt the pleasant presence of familiar neighbors in the houses all about me. It took effort to make my mind reach out with trust toward the future. Yet I found strength in knowing that we three would be meeting again within a week to go on threshing out this problem.

"There really must be a lot like us, the country over," I said to myself, and in a strangely vivid way that gave me a sense of security.

CHAPTER 5

I Tell a True Story

Another week had passed and we three were in Mary's front room. Like the whole house, it was filled with an air of family mahogany and of wide travel.

"Who wants to be first?" she asked.

Harriet didn't speak, so I looked at Mary and said, "You know me. I'm bursting with something. After you gave us that description of your elderly professor and her many interests, I wondered why I hadn't told you about my mother. Suddenly I seemed to see her as she used to busy herself in those later years, while she sat beside the full-length window of our first-floor living room. And I wanted to picture her to you."

"Why don't you?" asked Harriet, and I went on.

"Many friends and acquaintances," I said, "waved to her as they passed by the end of our little court. They expected her to be there, like a lighthouse. And she was that. With you both in mind I found myself thinking over the marvel of all she did in spite of physical handicaps. The next thing I knew I had typed several pages about her. They were headed 'Never a Shut-In.' I don't know why I'd never done it before."

Then I looked up at Harriet with a slightly defensive air.

"Of course," I said, "you're going to object, as you did about Mary's professor, that my mother didn't have to meet the rest home problems we've been dwelling on. And you'll be right. Her generation had an even greater dread of having to go to such a place, perhaps, than we have. Luckily, with nursing care, my father and sister were able to have her to the end as their companion in our home."

"How old was she?" Mary asked.

"She was eighty-seven when she died," I said, "and I believe that the majority of her activities, while she was in the seventies and eighties, could have been carried on by her almost as well in a rest home—certainly in spirit. As it was, her later years were for the most part spent in just one room, yet she would have merrily called to task anyone who named her a 'shut-in.' I'm sure that her imagination and will-power would have surmounted difficulties, wherever she lived, for she didn't know how to restrict her thoughts to her personal concerns. She would have found out the inner needs of the staff in a home and have given the whole place a lift."

I felt Harriet shifting into a relaxed position and I went on.

"For what it is worth to me," I said, "and for what it may be worth to you, I want to read this. You will see that Mother didn't defy old age; she went along with it. She had many keys to happiness, or maybe I should say that she opened many doors with her one happy key of continual service to others. As I was writing, I kept recalling one kind of thing after another. . . . How about it, Harriet?" I asked. "Will you admit her as evidence—evidence of a something that can be held fast in the face of growing old? It may take a good part of the afternoon."

"Who cares if it does!" Harriet answered.

I hardly had to glance at Mary's face, for I saw her settle back against the cushions, and I began:

NEVER A SHUT-IN

The "occupational therapy" of my mother's later years was planned by herself. Her fertile mind, her many skills, and her sympathetic heart needed no trained adviser in gerontology to outline busy-work for her. With hands so crippled by arthritis that she might well have folded them and watched the world go by, she typed frequent letters to people in need of getting mail. She kept on knitting and sewing, outwitting her gnarled fingers with the most delicate and certain stitches. When it began to hurt too much to use her forefinger for typing, she held a pencil in her stiffened hand and pumped the keys down with an even stroke of the eraser end. I believe that her sense of humor liked beating Mother Nature by sidestepping her handicaps.

In her disregard of physical annoyances, however sharp they might be, she used her head and her pluck. When the joint of the middle finger became too swollen for Mother to wear her thimble, she had the silversmith cut it down to a finger cap. And with that third of a thimble she made tiny rosebuds on a doll's sweater or a baby's bonnet. She knitted ever-changing patterns of useful things for humane purposes that kept her a woman of the world. If anyone were to ask me, "How many years was your mother shut in?" I should answer, " 'Years'? You could hardly count it in hours," for there was unfinished handiwork when she passed on to Other Service.

Her membership in the "In-Bed-Club" for cardiac children at the Massachusetts General Hospital in Boston gave her one of her most beloved outlets. When she saw a newspaper notice of the start of this club for children who had to be on their backs, often for many months, she became a charter member of the sponsoring group. But she didn't stop with that initial fee. She began dressing dolls for the bedridden little girls.

This, if I remember rightly, was at the time of Shirley Temple's early success in cinema. The young Shirley seemed almost doll-size and clever manufacturers were selling thousands of "Shirley Temple" dolls. These my mother started to dress for In-Bed-Club patients. She bought them wholesale from a Brooklyn factory, whose owner gave her a special discount when she told him where the dolls were to go. Indeed, I remember at least one big carton that came with his bill already receipted. And there also came, as a gift from this concern, a box of wardrobe trunks and clusters of little soft undershirts, such as are best made in quantity.

The trunks said "Shirley Temple" on them, and soon (for my mother's fingers flew with unbelievable swiftness) there were swinging on the miniature hangers clothes every doll needs, such as every little girl loves for herself. I recall a pongee sunsuit, piped with dark brown tape. A gay ski suit had tiny knitted mittens carefully fastened at the neck, a jaunty cap and, of all things, leather ski boots that would be the envy of a champion. Even the practical everyday dress of each wardrobe had some special touch. The party dress had featherstitching, or colored threads twisted into dots. Pajamas, of course, and a long dressing gown. All complete, all individual, all done by a mother's hands, a mother's imagination, a mother's heart.

At Woolworth's I bought a book of Shirley Temple paper dolls, picturing the notable little girl's actual clothes. My mother's quick eye caught up everything. Without making tracings, for the book patterns were far too small for the dolls, she cut her own patterns for exact copies in a way to amaze a trained draftsman. Often my sister did the machine-stitching and the pressing of the little garments, leaving Mother free for the designing and the many hand touches. So outstanding was her output that a museum invited her to dress a

Shirley Temple doll for their collection of period dolls, which reached back to the dolls of the children of early settlers.

During the First World War my mother was quite closely house-bound, but never a "shut-in" to herself. She began making articles for sale through gift shops or direct to patrons, so that she might earn money to adopt French war orphans. I think it was then that she began what she always called her "Lame Dog Fund." This was built up through such earnings, and then spent not only for orphans across the sea but for needy people nearer at hand. From time to time perhaps a friend would run in to see her and leave a bill or a check for this Lame Dog Fund.

The work that went to the gift shops from her crooked hands was as choice as that for the dolls. Everything met a high standard. An order came through a summer shop on Cape Cod for three sweaters to fit three little sisters of given ages. How beautifully she made these, with the flowered tips of their collars, each carefully graded for size. I recall my mother's writing to the proprietor that this order sounded like one from a doting grandmother. And the reply confirmed this, giving the grandmother's name—one well-known the country over.

Then there was another kind of venture which lasted well into my mother's old age. While she was still reasonably active, a friend of our family was approaching her eightieth birthday. My

mother said, "I believe I'll make a cake for Mrs.
N." Every year after that she would say, "I think I'll
make this one more cake for Mrs. N.," expecting
that it would be the last. What Mother "let herself
in for" became a matter of mirth as she kept up the
annual remembrance. For—and this is the truth—
when Mother herself was supposedly "old," she
made the twenty-fifth consecutive cake, for Mrs.
N.'s one-hundred-and-fourth birthday!

Now the cakes that went out from our house
were not ordinary; they were one of a kind. And
for this series Mother used her art at making pastry
flowers. I do not recall that she ever bothered with
a pastry tube. She used, rather, those deft fingers,
backed by that quick imagination and love of the
beautiful. A big round cake always, of course, and
white-frosted. As the years passed she ran the
gamut of her floral patterns, which were very true
to nature. I think the favorite with us all, and perhaps her favorite, too, was her wild-rose pattern.
She molded the raised pink petals of frosting with
a creative touch, even after her fingers looked too
stiff and reddened to manage. There were flat-
open blossoms, buds, half-open flowers—life-size,
with twinkles of yellow in the centers. And, as the
spray of blooms fell across the white circle, the
supporting stems with leaves of angelica or citron
were waiting for the petals to grow into place.

The wild rose was a favorite, but over the
years the cakes for Mrs. N. and for others took
many patterns. There was the daisy, with petals of

half-almonds; the violet with candied violets from the renowned store of S. S. Pierce (always fondly called "S. S. P.'s" by my mother); and the shamrocks for my father's birthday on St. Patrick's Day.

All this was Mother. And there were her many personal contacts by mail, by telephone, and with her callers. For, through years of suffering (we never knew how much) she kept a listening ear for what came to her of the troubles of others, and she did know how to give forth gracious words. In the letters that she tapped out on her typewriter she usually enclosed a typed copy of some bit of poetry or prose, to carry merriment or comfort, to relax or to spur. In defiance of all modern, improved typewriting equipment, Mother turned out an appalling amount of typing on an old-fashioned portable machine which rested on a small three-legged antique table set in front of her easy chair.

She wrote to people she knew and to many whom she didn't know. I recall a pleasing correspondence she had with a southern singer who gave regular Sunday afternoon concerts over one of the leading networks. He wrote to her when he became engaged and she followed the young couple for some years, without ever seeing them. At one time, she and my father were reading from Sir Wilfred Grenfell's *A Labrador Logbook* each night, and my mother wrote to tell Dr. Grenfell what his entries meant to them. From then on letters shuttled back and forth as long as he lived. She received one from him during the week of his death, I believe. His were filled with news of his work and almost invariably with a turn of the spiritual and a turn of the humorous. I can well think that she matched them in her way.

Long after *The Iron Woman* was written by Margaret Deland, my mother wrote a fan letter to the author to say that, on a rereading, this book certainly "held up." In the course of time a limousine came to our door. Mrs. Deland and her companion had driven out to meet this unknown correspondent, and there began a beautiful friendship. Mrs. Deland sent my mother an advance manuscript copy of her autobiography. I think that she felt in my mother's love for my father the counterpart of her love for her Lorin, who was no longer living. So each of these women won a friend for later-year enjoyment.

People became forgetful of Mother's physical condition as soon as they saw her radiant face or heard her steady voice. For this reason visitors readily told her their troubles. I remember Mother's smiling when one had left.

"Mrs. So-and-so plumped a vigorous kiss on my mouth while she was trying to tell me what a terrible sore throat she was undergoing," my mother told us.

Physical sore throats and mental and spiritual sore throats, too, were brought to her sympathetic "clinic." She was wise, patient. She knew whether the seeker needed fortitude, repentance, self-forgetfulness, faith, or a downright good laugh. She had sorted over these assets for her own life, and experience had not only taught her but made her a teacher.

Younger women came, more often than not with their children. Under my mother's couch-bed in the room where she spent her days were several large suit boxes, filled with toys for every age. A young visitor always remembered this and threw back the cover to rediscover his or her favorite playthings. And while the miniature meat grinder or carpet sweeper or other toy friends were being enjoyed, the child's mother rediscovered my mother. The young family went away refreshed and, I am sure, feeling that they had refreshed their hostess.

Mother had, too, a telephone list of people who were really shut-in's—some, perhaps, because of chronic illness; some returned home from the hospital; or others, "suffering" from old age. These she would call, listening to their complaints of last night's sleeplessness, of the new or old aches, of the neglect and loneliness that were overcoming them. Often they called her, in the pleasant security that she would be at home. As she always liked to answer the telephone, which was beside her, she allowed herself no escape. A querulous voice was never told that Mother "was not able to talk today." She lifted the receiver with the air of being ready to shake hands with someone.

All through her life my mother wrote verse,

which appeared in various periodicals, and she never stopped up this outlet. This serious poem about old age, which was published in *The Christian Century,* speaks for itself:

Occupation

Age has not passed me by without his toll
Of strength from eye and ear,
But, with a gracious gesture,
Leaves in every ravaged spot
A thousand miracles of glad surprise—
An answered prayer, a friendship new,
The touch of loving hands, a child's gay voice,
A sacrament of pouring oil and wine
In this sad world—clouding the stars with hate.
Oh, may the Heavenly One who rules both age and time
Give me the grace to lively live,
That I shall not the end anticipate,
Throwing His gift of occupation to the winds;
So Gabriel, when he comes, must loudly call me from my
     work,
Not find me whining at the Outer Gate!

SARAH AVERY FAUNCE

Mary and Harriet had hardly stirred while I was reading and, when I finished, they were quiet. So was I. Then Harriet spoke.

"There's Sue Reinhardt for you—plus!" she said.

"Yes," agreed Mary. "They must both have found

something big to depend on . . . before they came into old age. You can be sure of that. Something much higher than themselves."

Harriet and Mary rose as I made a gesture of leaving. Somehow I didn't want to say any more and I felt that they didn't expect me to.

CHAPTER 6

———

We Face Cold Facts

Once again we were together in my apartment where, I confess, I was making the most of one day at a time. Ever since that first visit to The Walden I had been hugging my present way of living in the fear that an end might come to it. Now I felt that I had partly thrown off this dread and I settled into a somewhat more comfortable mood.

As I welcomed Mary and Harriet, I showed a different kind of ease and I knew it. There was a quiet cheer about them, too, that met me a good halfway.

"I've kept thinking about your mother," Mary said.

"Thanks," I said. "So have I."

"Do you know what?" Harriet said, leaning forward eagerly as she sat down. "She's done something to me. From now on everything we think or say is bound to be colored by your portrait of her."

Then she turned to me with a dare in her look.

"But it's not going to make me dress dolls," she declared. "Don't ever expect that! She had grace, didn't she? And by the way, I looked up that word."

"You would, being an English teacher," I said.

"Of course we know that Shakespeare didn't mean salvation or anything like that. For us the best meaning I found was 'any characteristic fitted to confer pleasure or benefit.'"

Mary picked this up.

"'Confer pleasure,'" she repeated, taking out her knitting. "That is surely out-giving and, too, I think it covers receiving. Some people accept what others really want to do for them, but without too much grace. I have an older friend who always says, 'You ought not to do that for me!' no matter how slight a thing I've done. And it always draws me back into my shell."

"Probably she doesn't like feeling indebted to anyone," observed Harriet. "I know how that is. And I hate to have Eileen's children do kindnesses for me, especially when I feel sure she's put them up to it. Maybe it's good for them, though," she admitted. "And perhaps I'm sometimes at fault for taking the pleasure out of their friendliness. I don't believe I've thought about that."

"Remember how grudging Janet Coombs was in accepting your flowers?" I suggested.

"Yes, I do," Harriet answered. "Watching her is one way of learning," she admitted, as if to herself.

I must say I thought Harriet was making a wonderful beginning. When she had come into the room, I had noticed that she didn't seem to be moving any better, yet somehow she didn't allow her lameness to be so much of a disability. Her apparent change quickened me, and now I dared to let myself out a little.

"Speaking of learning," I stated, "I've decided that, since I am only sixty-eight, I'm going to hope for at least seven years before I have to use my *Declaration of Dependence* on the threshold of a rest home. And I've been thinking," I went on, "about two friends of mine on their country estate in Pennsylvania. The husband was a landscape architect, and they plotted improvements on their acreage to run through a Ten-Year Plan. I visited them in their year of rose planting. The newly set bushes looked like nothing at all to me. But they were an illustration of practical forethought and intelligent faith on the part of the owners. Years later, I saw the realization of that faith in all its abundance. So I am ambitious now," I explained, "if you see what I mean, to work out a Seven-Year Plan. I need it."

"You mean," suggested Mary, "you're planning to set out an orchard in the hope of having apples to pick by the time you go to live somewhere else. 'More than enough to grow on,' as my professor put it."

"Apples remind me," I said and I slipped out to my kitchenette to get coffee. "Don't talk till I come back," I called.

As I set the tray onto my table, I watched Harriet getting up to come for her cup. She let no sign of pain flash across her face. I couldn't quite believe that her arthritis had been cured and I said to myself, "So Harriet has been practicing in her way." I wanted to say this out loud, but I didn't. It just gave me a feeling that together we three might make what Mary had called a "forward swing into this Thing."

"Wouldn't that be something?" I thought.

"I'll tell you what I wish," Harriet remarked as she began to sip her coffee. "I'd like to know the plain facts of our problem so that we can understand the actual aspects of what we're facing. Seems to me we've been talking in the air, except for what we saw with our own eyes at The Walden. I've told you that I've been into these places, but I've never thought of them for myself, not like this. Never.

"To come right down to it for me," she urged, "is there any home near enough to Eileen for her convenience where I could go? That's what I ought to find out. Is there a choice of homes? What do they charge and what are their requirements for entrance? For all I know, I'm not even eligible anywhere."

Mary set down her cup with a decided smile.

"Harriet Barnes," she exclaimed, "I knew you were going to bring us to this point. I've felt it coming from the start. And, believe it or not," she went on, "I haven't let any grass grow under my feet. I've been hard at work all these weeks, and now here are these folders of the information I've scouted for throughout our vicinity. I'm just beginning to see what it adds up to. I only wish I could bequeath my house to the town for a rest home—the kind we need, endowed and all. But it has to go to John's nephew. We three girls could be the charter residents."

"You might not want me," laughed Harriet, "at least till I've had those seven years of prep work we're talking about."

Then she looked at Mary with admiring warmth.

"It's so like you, you old social worker," she said, staring at Mary's bulging briefcase playfully. "Information, data, statistics. I suppose you've gotten each one of us placed somewhere with a room and bath and private porch."

"What *is* the hope for us, Mary?" I asked, and I could feel that my voice sounded anxious.

"There's more to it than you might think," she replied. "To begin with, there aren't many places. There isn't one spot here in town. Being a resident here doesn't do one thing for you. And it seems that for many homes you do have to be a resident of the town, sometimes for as long as ten years prior to application."

I got up to put a card table where Mary might spread out her papers.

"Or," she went on, "you may have to belong to the religious or other organization that endowed or supports the home."

"Excuse me, if I jump ahead," I interrupted, "but when you do find a place with requirements you might meet, is there any chance of a vacancy?"

"That's just it," Mary answered me. "There's a long waiting list everywhere. I got circulars and questionnaires and so forth and I telephoned for answers to questions raised in my mind. The common reply they gave was that there were no vacancies and they didn't know when there would be. The director of one 'Home for Aged Women' said, 'I'd advise applying soon rather than late, as we do have a list. It takes at least one year—perhaps two or more —before anyone can be admitted.'

"Some homes," Mary continued, "fill applications in

order of receipt. They have to, if the home is town-owned or otherwise under public control. But a few do consider all the applications on hand at the time a vacancy occurs. For instance," she explained, taking up an illustrated folder, "here's a privately endowed home that offers a given vacancy to the woman on their list who seems most to need the Home physically and financially and, at the same time, gives promise of being acceptable to the group."

"There you go!" put in Harriet. "That's the 'grace and good disposition' of it." She paused, then went on. "So you didn't find dozens of ideal places longing to send us engraved invitations?"

I looked from Harriet to Mary and seemed now to feel in them the very uneasiness I was giving in to as we began to face everything down.

"How old do you have to be when you apply?" I asked.

"I found some places with residents as young as sixty-five, or even younger," replied Mary.

"According to that," decided Harriet, "I ought to enter an application everywhere before sunset today."

"It does give you a feeling that there's so little time," I said, "doesn't it?"

"We can't afford to get panicky about it," advised Mary, "but I do think we should all register our names in several places. As one director put it to me over the telephone, 'You should have several strings out.'"

"Let's make it the same strings," urged Harriet, and I couldn't help sharing her unspoken hope that we three might be together. She went on wistfully, "If only you could turn your house into a rest home, Mary, you could open up for friends first!"

"If only!" Mary said. "I must say I found a lot of things I'd do, *if only.* I like to imagine leaving a generous endowment to carry on with. And I found some ideal phrases to use in my will."

"Such as?" I asked.

"Here's one: a home in trust given by a woman whose will said, 'I have felt the need of a place, other than a hospital or an institution, where a helpless or partially helpless adult woman, or a lonely woman of refinement, might have some of the care and comforts of a home at a reasonable expense or, in some cases, free of expense.'"

"Wonderful!" exclaimed Harriet.

"Or here's a place that states its purpose 'to provide shelter, security, and companionship in a home for women who are no longer able to maintain a comfortable home for themselves.'"

"That kind of wording does bring more than a crumb of comfort right now," suggested Harriet. "Go on with that imaginary Mary Olmstead Trust. I am applying right now."

"Well, I'd like this kind of thing truly said of it," smiled Mary and she read from a booklet: " 'The Home is filling a great need in the lives of the residents. It is taking the place of family, friends, and home to those who would otherwise be bereft of these blessings.'"

"That says it," I remarked.

"I wish," Mary went on, "that I could leave a place— or start one now, for that matter—that would be like this: 'Thoughtful and affectionate care of the family is the ideal of the management. Nothing that can be done for the welfare and needs of the residents is left undone.' And I would hope that my booklet could promise 'single rooms where requirements as to heat, light, and ventilation may be arranged according to personal preference.' But that is rare. You can look through these pamphlets, but first let me pick a few choice bits; they are that cheering! For example: 'Attractive living rooms, sun parlor, and spacious porches are available to all—and garden and croquet lawn.'"

"Perhaps I could garden at that one," Harriet said, moving over to the table to see the circular.

Mary read from another before she passed it over: "'Three large open porches . . . a cheerful dining room where pastel greens and soft rose form the background for leisurely meals, graciously served . . . congenial conversation before the open fire in the living room.'"

Harriet looked through these illustrations and showed them to me.

"There are your white hairdos, like those at The Walden," she teased.

I saw the residents sitting in rockers and garden swings, but somehow they didn't scare me this time.

"Do you know . . . it may be a lot to admit . . . but," I said hesitantly, "I think I'm getting a little used to the idea . . . the idea of everything, I mean."

I felt Harriet giving me a sharp, appraising glance; but I went on quietly.

"I guess they all let you take some of your own furniture," I observed. "A chair, a lamp, or even your bed, this circular says."

"Like Sue's desk and her Venetian glass," Mary said, and she fingered one more pamphlet.

"I think," she went on, "I'll quote this word for word in the requirements for the Mary Olmstead Trust, as Harriet calls it: 'The Home expects its family to manifest the spirit and to practice the virtues of a household in which loyalty and forbearance are taken for granted and individual rights are subordinated to the common good.'"

"That was what I intended to cover in my Declaration of Dependence," I said.

"All right," Harriet declared, "if you're both trying to preach to me, I'll take it. I'd better practice on 'forbearance' at Eileen's if I'm to qualify for your place, Mary. But don't think," she added, "that I've had too sudden a change of heart—today, that is. When you come down to it, I've felt myself changing, or wanting to change, ever since I saw Sue Reinhardt. . . . And then," she said, turning to me, "there's your mother."

CHAPTER 7

We Face Hard Facts, Too!

After a break for coffee, Mary went on. "For this Mary Olmstead Home," she said, "I shall have to think over the financial requirements. It appears that you don't 'pay your money and take your choice,' not by any means. You pay your money according to the choice of some donor or group of administrators."

"What do these places charge, anyway?" Harriet asked.

"The cost varies considerably," answered Mary, sifting through her papers. "Here is a boarding-home that expects regular board by the week according to the room you have or according to your income, and you are supposed to be able to go to the dining room."

"Under your own steam," put in Harriet.

"At the Family Service Agency where I turned for help in my hunt," continued Mary, "they told me that the boarding-home basis is getting more common with the increase in old age benefits, but such homes aren't too plentiful around here yet."

I went to my desk to get paper and pencil for myself and for Harriet, too.

"You may want to take notes on this," I suggested. "Go on, Mary," I said, but Harriet came in with a loud exclamation as she stared at a circular that Mary had passed over to her.

"Horrors!" she said, starting to read. " '*Fee*. No definite fee is stated, but just as the applicant needs what the Home can give in care, comfort, and pleasant environment during her lifetime, so the Home needs whatever financial help can be given by the applicant. Each person'—listen to this —'each person must assign to the Home, on entrance, whatever money, investments, and personal property she now owns or may hereafter acquire or become entitled to.' "

"Yes," admitted Mary, "I was going to come to that type, for that is the money method of many homes. This one specifies a flat payment on your entering, however. And that cares for you the rest of your days, while any income you may have is yours."

"But the rest of them expect you to give up everything," commented Harriet, "except your own name."

"If I had to go onto the take-everything basis for this home we are imagining," Mary said, "I think I'd copy a hint from this booklet: 'An individual agreement will be made with each member, whereby she will have available money for reasonable personal expenses.' A number of them say plainly that they give back an allowance for spending money."

"Then they do manage to pass back a little," observed

Harriet, and I wondered for a moment whether this realistic talk she had asked for wasn't getting on her nerves after all.

"I hope to goodness it covers clothing," I said, and I knew my voice must show that this whole financial slant had come as a shock to me.

Mary looked with that wonderful calm of hers first at one of us, then at the other.

"But when you really think of it," she said, "there isn't much of any other arrangement they can make. They take a gamble on each one of us, as to how long we may live and how much care we may become during those years."

"And," said Harriet, "at the same time they really take on your financial cares. They fix it so that you can just settle down with no more worry about tax returns or anything."

I must say this appealed to me for I hate the arithmetic of accounts and always have.

"No more reconciling of bank statements," I enthused. "Harriet, you're almost winning me over. Especially when I recognize that it is quite likely my brain may tire more and more easily. I surely would adore right now having someone to lean on without any more budgeting or paying bills or checking of income. If you don't have younger relatives to look out for those things for you, as I don't— well, there it is. You can't expect to lean on a reliable institution without giving them something to lean on. I can see that."

"Ye-es!" said Harriet and I began to feel something refreshing in that room. It was as though all three of us had come up for air and were breathing more easily at the notion of "giving over." I could tell that they, too, were welcoming our improvement, though nobody exactly said, "We're progressing, aren't we?"

After fingering through several more booklets, Harriet noted, "They all make mention of our need for companionship. I suppose that's why they speak of entertainments, projects, clubs, and so forth. 'Social and occupational life,' this one calls it. I dare say I shall submit to being organized. At any rate, it will be a change from having Eileen's Den of Cub Scouts come to the house, with all their precious racket," she admitted and she let out a real laugh.

Mary laughed, too, and then said, "Naturally, I didn't look into the apartment hotel as a refuge, which I for one can't afford."

"Even if you could," I said, "you might not like it too well. A certain kind of care is taken of you, at the price. You can ring for a bellboy but it isn't the same thing, say, as having a trained attendant on call. And if you have a companion of your own, up shoots the expense. I don't know that I envy anyone who can afford that kind of living anyway. They can have it."

Harriet glanced up as though an idea had come over her.

"There are worse things then," she said very slowly, "than this we're contemplating! Now what else are you going to tell us, Mary?"

"Well," replied Mary, "of course there's the matter of a physical examination. Usually you have to offer a statement that you are fit for entrance, show no signs of chronic illness or tendencies that would make you too serious a charge to take care of. Some places require this examination to be made by their own physician. You see these that I looked into are definitely not what are called nursing homes, although even rest homes do often have infirmaries for temporary illnesses and occasionally for a chronic case."

"I guess arthritis," said Harriet, "is too common for them to refuse. If not, I'm done for before I begin to apply."

"But of course, Harriet," said Mary, "if you apply they assume that you have a measure of incapacity—if it is only a lack of vigor to go out for meals or to get them for yourself. That is, I am speaking of those of us who are our own housekeepers."

"In other words, no matter what they are called, these are Old Ladies' Homes," said Harriet.

"And some old ladies need homes," I added, "long before others. As Janet Coombs told us, you don't know who'll be hit first."

"Aren't you getting back to a rather depressing key?" Harriet reproved.

"Forgive me, both of you," I apologized. "We've been going forward, and now I've thrown us into reverse."

Harriet nodded and then said, "If you ask me, I think each one of us ought to make application right now at The Walden. Don't think I'm silly. They must have a waiting list a mile long. I shan't sleep a wink until I sign myself in there. How about you two?"

"I knew we'd come to that," Mary said.

"What about our going around to visit other places?" I asked her.

"We can do that," she answered. "However, the director of one of the nicest of these homes told me over the telephone that they don't receive visitors like us. That is, the home isn't open for inspection. Their idea is that every woman there is a guest, as in a private home. If a visitor is shown to their rooms, this breaks in on their privacy."

"You can just imagine," interrupted Harriet, "having a lot of strangers peering in on you. It's your little house— that's what your room amounts to."

"I don't believe," I put in, "that Miss Holden would have shown everyone around The Walden as thoroughly as she did us, but she knew we were Sue's friends and she could tell the women so."

"Perhaps not, but here's another thing," said Mary. "This director I mentioned was very friendly but he kept us at our distance. He went on to explain that they don't show visitors even the common living rooms. 'Our guests may be sitting there reading or enjoying the television,' he said, 'and this is their home.' "

"I say, let's apply at that place, too," urged Harriet. "I like the sound of it."

A grave shadow of hesitation came over Mary's face.

"The trouble is, he didn't want to tell me how many names are already on their list, but he was the one who said, 'You should have several strings out. You don't know where a place may be available at your moment of need,' he put it."

"What about this state-aided housing project for the elderly that's on foot here in town?" I asked Mary. "Is there anything in it for us?"

"Those are going to be compact apartments such as are springing up here and there, with state or even federal assistance," Mary replied. "They are all right for lots of people who are now living in housekeeping quarters that are too inconvenient or too expensive for them to manage for necessary comfort. My own next step will come when I am not able to do household tasks. That means a rest home, free of care. And, what's more important, as we've been saying, I want someone close by to have an eye on me."

"The same here," I said, helping Mary stack the booklets together. "I have a small enough apartment for as long as it and I can keep going together. Then I shall need someone to take the place of the family I don't have. That's why it begins to look possible for me to yield at any point, for security's sake."

"And I," said Harriet, "don't have to be told that I'm really pretty much depending on Eileen for almost everything. Though I try to help some, I know that I am already dependent to a large degree. And I might as well say right now," she added, "that I'm almost getting to want to see what this business would be like."

"And this from you, Harriet!" I exclaimed, not without sudden admiration.

She didn't backtrack, but she did give a little low whistle.

"There is surely a lot to think over," she said. "I'm glad you did all this spadework for us, Mary. Now at least we aren't 'flying blind' any more."

"It would be my idea," I said, looking gratefully at Mary, "that churches and do-good organizations in any locality where there isn't an old age center might look into this kind of thing and keep an up-to-date directory. I mean so that people as unknowing as we were could get thorough information about the situation in their neighborhood. Not everyone will have a trained scout like you for a friend, Mary."

"I did get some help from our Family Service Agency, as I told you," Mary said. "Such agencies in many places are ready to give assistance. They know how to learn facts from doctors, clergy, nurses, families who have members living in homes, and from reliable avenues of 'hearsay.' In this field I never combed a vicinity where I was doing social work the way I've done here for us, because I always worked in child welfare. But now these details come close."

I saw a deep smile of satisfaction steal over her face and wondered whether it was from some pleasant recollection of her vocation or whether perhaps Mary herself was beginning to enjoy our new attitude.

"I should think it would be hard for a social agency to appraise these places, and to advise," I remarked.

"It makes a demand like child placement," said Mary. "You have to be on your guard in accepting adverse criticism about a home. It may be that many are not too near perfection. But reports about a single incident sometimes prejudice people falsely, and become greatly enlarged. On the other hand, you can't condone anything less than good care, good food, and such cleanliness as is not always found. Weighing of information is very difficult because it has to be secondhand."

"Wouldn't you love to start dozens of places such as we girls need and endow them this very minute?" I asked impulsively.

"That's it," Harriet agreed. "Here we are facing this.

And it looks to me not like just calling out, 'Rest Home, ho!' but like shouting, 'Rest Home, ho! if there's any rest home to *ho to!*'"

"In the light of the waiting lists I've run into and the vacancies I haven't run into," said Mary, "it looks to me, Harriet, as though you might have to quiet down and stay with Eileen for some time. There are plenty of other young families who'll be keeping their elders with them, too."

"But isn't that the right and wise thing for some people?" I asked, turning to Mary's experienced mind for an answer.

She leaned forward in her chair and, after a pause, said, "If it is right for the family as a whole, then it's right for the grandmother or the elderly aunt or whoever it may be."

"I know it can be done," Harriet volunteered, "but I don't intend to try to prove it indefinitely. It's more than just a mutual give-and-take. I've seen situations myself where older people fitted in and were even an asset, but for myself I do believe that I should weigh my needs with unselfishness against the needs of Eileen and Tom and their growing children. The youngsters are bound to suffer if too much attention is given from the middle generation to an oldster in the family group."

"I believe," said Mary, "that some younger people are overconscientious about not letting an older relative go to a home, even if she wants to. I've seen women who were really much happier with their own age group. It does take adapting, or that overused word *adjusting*, but so does living with the younger folks, as Harriet says."

"You mean," asked Harriet, "that young couples are

afraid of the way it will 'look' to the neighbors, if they 'put' Mother or Father in a home? Like neglect or hard-heartedness, that is?"

"I believe," answered Mary, "both sides have to measure this with courage and with candor—and with love—without any feeling that this is strange or peculiar to their lives. It isn't an unusual move."

I interrupted here to take a cushion over to tuck behind Harriet's back. By the way she kept shifting her position, it looked as though this whole afternoon had truly taken hold of her. To myself I thought, however reluctantly, "We really aren't young, and we are all passing through a sort of shock."

But aloud I said, "It's really funny in a way, but entering a home is a master stroke of *in*dependence, if you do it willingly."

"Yes," Harriet said, "and that's why I'm convinced that the initial suggestion should come from the older person. I mean to talk with Eileen, now that we are all going to make applications. I think I'll tell her that this will give me a chance to live a life of my own again—in a new way, that is."

The next moment I was very proud of Harriet. "That woman has brains and she has a heart," I said to myself.

For this was what she said, in a low thoughtful voice. "Perhaps what seems like a sacrifice could open out privilege and friendship beyond imagining. That's what I'm going to say to Eileen. For the sake of my young people I'm determined to take the adventure when an opening can be found. And it's my firm idea that, when you insist on leaving the young home, you should mean what you say.

That is, you should be wholly sincere, hard though it may be to take some of the details of the break. I mean you shouldn't say sweetly that you think it's best for everyone concerned—and then be ready with barbs or kickers to the contrary, the way Janet Coombs would do."

"The barb is too likely to stick out at the wrong time," offered Mary.

"And if you get yourself to the point of really meaning it," I said, "you won't gripe when they come to see you or when you go back to see them. You won't tell them how very lonely you are, the way some people do. Not if you have what it takes, you won't."

"That's right," said Harriet. "There must be ways of meeting loneliness. If young relatives have any feeling for you, and certainly my Eileen has, they know such a move isn't easy."

"The mother of one of my friends is in a rest home and she has her grandchildren's mending brought there for her to do," I said.

"That wouldn't cure me of anything," laughed Harriet, "but I see your meaning."

For a second I thought she was going to bring in those Walden aprons again, but they seemed to have ceased worrying her. Instead she turned to me.

"You look as though you have something up your sleeve," she urged.

"I have," I said. "I brought a little verse of mine that I want to read to you and to Mary. It was published some years ago in a book for children, but I've changed it some for our purpose. Remember, that first day we were together,

Mary spoke of dreading to reduce her possessions to one roomful. I thought of this verse at that time. Here it is:

The Smallest Perch

Song Sparrow, with his streakéd breast,
  Sings gaily from a twig or post.
The smallest perch that he can find
  Is where he seems to sing the most.
He lights upon a pile of brush
  Or any common kind of place,
His spirit fully satisfied
  With just one inch of singing-space."

Mary gave me a quick, penetrating glance, which I wasn't to understand for some days. She did not speak, but Harriet had to give one of her last words.

"The idea being," she pointed out, as though we didn't see it, "that one inch is enough, provided you use it for singing."

CHAPTER 8
———

To The Walden Again

The next morning Harriet telephoned: "I've been talking with Mary Olmstead and, if you say so, we wish you'd
make a date with The Walden for tomorrow for us to go
to see Sue. Sue and Janet, I mean. Mary tells me the more
she thinks about them, the more she thinks they need us,"
she added.

"Or perhaps we need them," I suggested.

Harriet's voice sounded eager, and I couldn't help
noticing that neither of us used those former cold words
of ours about "making a visitation." Now we were going
to friends, and friends we felt near to, not only out of compassion for them but also out of a new understanding of
our own future. As on our other visit, Mary came in her
car with Harriet.

"It was that verse of yours about the sparrow and his
inch of singing-space that made me want to go over to those
two again," Mary said. "My roomy house with all our treas-

ured possessions makes me hurt when I think of those one-room people."

"I'll tell you what it is," I said. "When we three get together, we're only talking. With them, all this is the real thing. Maybe the closer we draw to them, the more clearly we're going to see and think for ourselves, if that doesn't sound too goody-goody!"

"After all," said Mary, as we drove along, "preparing for old age shouldn't be so different from the way we handle the rest of life. We expect to train for teaching, for social work, for marriage, for childbearing and child-rearing. Everyone thinks it's good sense to look ahead like that. Life comes in chunks, one chunk after another, and we try to get ready to nibble at the next chunk without being caught unaware and without resisting what we come to."

"I guess it's when you try to hide your head that you get hit," said Harriet. "I'm glad we're looking straight at this thing now."

It is hard to put into words the contrast between our attitude in Mary's car that afternoon and our air of banter the first time we had headed for The Walden. Today we made no effort to screen our feelings from each other.

Without asking for Miss Holden, I told the attendant we'd like to be shown to Mrs. Reinhardt's room, that she was expecting us. I felt a trifle guilty because I knew that, as before, we would be passing Janet's door. But I noticed that Mary and Harriet didn't stop me. It was my guess that they, too, found Janet a puzzle. It wasn't so much that we wanted to manage her and didn't know how, but that we didn't know how to manage ourselves when we were with her. Sue called out for us to come in and promptly introduced to us a personable young woman who was standing by the table with several small packages.

"This is Linda Taylor, one of the friends from the Guild who does errands for us," Sue said. "I can't see what we'd do without them. We count on having someone come every Friday, rain or shine. It isn't that any one of us wants much shopping done," she explained, "but we do run out of thread or hair nets or"—and here her eyes twinkled—"lipstick and rouge."

Sue reached for a little mirror and tried a new lipstick with her head on one side.

"Precisely the right shade, thanks," she said to Linda. Then, turning to us, she went on with amusement, "You know 'they' say we shouldn't let ourselves down. And unless we're lucky enough to have relatives or these younger friends who come regularly, we can't keep the pace. In a way we're on a desert island."

This was the only little sign of complaint we had heard from Sue, and I was glad to find her so human.

"Linda belongs to the church choir that comes to sing here for us, and the Guild members take us to church services when we can go. May I tell them, Linda, what you did for us last week?"

Linda made a gesture with both hands as though it was nothing much.

"She came and got three of us," Sue said, "for a tea party at her home. It wasn't just a cup of tea with crackers. Linda brought in a lovely great silver tray with her best cups, and a beautiful pattern they were. There was a green glass plate stacked with fancy sandwiches she had made.

The cream-cheese ones were round with a dainty sprig of green flying at the center."

Here Linda tried to speak, but Sue went on.

"Those with a watercress filling were rolled and tied with green ribbon. Then there were special cookies and colored mints. It did our eyes and our hearts good, Linda. You gave us something fresh to think about for days. Those were touches they don't have time for here, and we know it. But, more than those sandwiches, we enjoyed having the three boys run in from school, full of push and busyness. Too much racket for us to take all the time, but entertaining for those few moments."

I felt Mary looking at me, and Harriet, too. I read what was in their faces. We three all felt more than ever guilty at our earlier neglect of our two friends. What was uniting us, too, I think, was a feeling of forgiveness toward the Guild for the cardboard ducks and for the rabbits at Easter. Perhaps some of the members had to express themselves in that way.

"You're more faithful than Mrs. Reinhardt's schoolmates," Harriet apologized.

"Yes," added Mary, "you put us to shame."

"There's nothing to be ashamed about," Sue said quickly, "there are lots of things you don't even think of until you've been through an experience yourself. These young women happen to have extra imagination and some how or other they *make* time to look out for us."

Sue stood up to say goodby and I saw in her all the grace of the Kentucky hostess she must have been—and still was.

Linda smiled and said, "You all seem to be overlooking the fact that Mrs. Reinhardt has come to mean more to me than I can ever mean to the whole of The Walden. I've even brought her my troubles, haven't I?" she added, backing toward the door just as a determined knock came.

There stood Janet, supported by her two canes.

"How perfectly lovely of you to come again so soon!" she gushed, edging herself into Sue's own chair. "Let me see, it was about a month ago, or even more, that you were here, wasn't it?" she asked; and I, for one, felt the barb the way she intended it.

"I suppose Sue has told you about the terrible night we all had here last night," she began, as Linda disappeared.

No, Sue hadn't, we all said. What we meant was, Sue wouldn't.

"It's really been more than one night. It's been a whole series," went on Janet, and I could see that nothing was going to stop her. "What's more, you don't know when an end will come to it, either. I'm really not able to . . . sustain . . . it," she sighed.

I felt Harriet draw back in horror at what we were getting into.

"You see, there's a woman over there in the infirmary," Janet pressed on, "and with the windows and everything open we know every bit she's going through, and if anyone in this place gets a wink of sleep, I'd like to know who it is. It'd be a blessing to be deaf."

This was too much for Sue.

"Why, Janet," she reproved, "you'll wish it onto yourself, if you don't look out!"

"Well, you ought to know what I mean," insisted Janet.

"Why you haven't got dark circles under your eyes I for one don't see. To feel that someone's suffering, and you can't do a thing to drown out those sounds, and you may be in her position any day yourself."

I didn't dare to look at either Mary or Harriet. It seemed to me that we had been hurled into the very grimness of it all. Yet . . . yet . . . there was Sue's face right before us, and I could remember other restful faces as we had made our way through the sunroom a few moments before. I was relieved to have Harriet speak.

"I should think that such a case belonged in a nursing home, or a hospital, not in a rest home like this," she said with that anxious frown on her forehead.

Sue answered quickly.

"The Walden happens to be the type of home," she explained, "where an infirmary can take care of a few of us who may become critically ill. The woman Janet mentions has lived here so long that it is wonderful for her not to have to move, and the infirmary is away from the rest of us. Only sometimes, as with last night, we do know what is going on there in part."

"How do you ever surmount it?" asked Harriet eagerly.

"It does take practice," Sue admitted thoughtfully.

"She means it happens often," interrupted Janet, "but of course Sue would say not to borrow trouble."

"Perhaps I would, Janet," Sue said with a kindly accent. "I do know that in a place like this you have to accustom yourself to happenings you'd like to run away from, but just can't."

As I held my glance on Sue, her even temper really got me. She had that same calm voice I had noticed before.

Sue seemed plain good, facing things realistically but without getting ruffled, the way I remembered her in school.

"Yes," she went on, and she seemed to be changing the subject on purpose, "you have to accept many circumstances. At first it was hard for me to get used to falling in with the routine. You learn that many things have to be planned for the benefit of everyone and the individual can't have any choice about going along with the regime. And yet see what we receive in exchange for giving over our freedom of choice. At the very same time, we're freed of many decisions that make active life so difficult to ride, especially at our age. We've left a lot of everyday trials and problems behind us. Here we need never feel that we've lost our freedom in the real sense, for true freedom is of the spirit."

Sue, I thought, was evading Harriet's worry about surmounting the strain of others' suffering. Yet I couldn't help trusting her to come back to it.

"One day," she went on, "after I'd been here a while and was still resisting, I did what was for me a very natural thing. I turned to my Bible and in the gospel of St. Matthew I came to the words, 'And there was a great calm.'"

I believe this was the first time that Sue or any of us had mentioned the Bible or anything religious and I spoke of it. Sue smiled with assurance.

"Don't let me sound pious," she begged, "but I call the Bible the handy reference book for the rest home. You know, like the cookbook for the kitchen or," turning to me, "the dictionary for the writer. Some of my favorite recipes are here," she said, handing me a cloth-bound copy of the Book of Psalms.

As I opened it, I saw many markings in the margins. But what struck me was the very large type—my first intimation of Sue's failing eyesight. She had not imposed on us the slightest inkling of this. Out of such patience, anything Sue might see fit to say would be welcome.

"Now that you have me started," she said, motioning for Janet to lean back in the easy chair, "I'll tell you what I notice here—that the most contented and livable people brought religious faith with them. Of course, beliefs vary, but the common basis for us all has to be faith in a Supreme Being. By that I mean for myself a simple faith in God. I've seen the need of that proved under this roof over and over again. Some women don't talk easily about such things; they aren't built that way. Yet, if they have a sincere, trustful belief, you see it in their eyes."

"That's exactly what I was thinking a few minutes ago," I said, but I didn't explain that I meant Sue's own eyes.

"When I see this expression, I'm often reminded of one of my stand-by verses from those Psalms," Sue went on as I returned the book to her, " 'They looked unto Him and were radiant.' I believe I must like radiance."

"Not the Pollyanna kind," put in Harriet.

"Definitely not," agreed Sue, "though if you ask me I think that is better than none at all. The people here who have no sparkle one of my friends calls the Glums."

"I wonder," remarked Harriet, "whether they change —improve their agreeableness, that is."

From this half-question I guessed that Harriet was taking a lesson from Sue, as I was. Somehow I had found myself a little self-conscious at this turn into a discussion of religious faith. I stole a look at Janet while this was going on; it seemed as though she felt caught by something and she wasn't sure whether she could, to use her own word, "sustain" this kind of conversation.

Then I understood why Sue had broken in so almost abruptly with what was so intimate to her. She had been wanting to share her own radiant solution of rest home problems with Janet. Now she had a chance to talk *around* Janet, without seeming to talk *at* her or even *with* her. So I wasn't surprised to have Sue go ahead. And the more she said the more satisfied I was that we had come. Not only for our sakes, but because she had plainly been thinking a great deal about these higher things, and it must be doing her good now to be able to let herself out.

"Yes, Harriet, they do change," she said. "I've seen women come here bitter and almost like rebels. Gradually it comes over some of them that you can't live here without a clear, workable faith. You aren't able to push around old ways *in* old ways any longer. You have to turn to something bigger than yourself because your life becomes naturally more restricted as you grow older and you need largeness of soul and firm beliefs to roam around in. You really do have to become a new creature. Yet it's all so simple," Sue tried to tell us, "and many make it so hard."

Then she went on eagerly, "I've often seen people struggling, and I mean long before I came here. And they struggle honestly, too. Perhaps they fight to find some so-called 'intellectual' pattern to follow. They are determined to find a definitely bounded belief that is absolutely doubt-proof—and all at once, without allowing time for it to grow.

"But belief," she pressed on, "belief is like the pattern of leaves on a sunny lawn. It is often quiet and can be traced to the last detail. Then the wind blows and the pattern shifts and changes, even though the same reliable sun is going on its orderly way." She paused and then said, "I think that God, like the sun, goes His orderly way, and the variations we see in the pattern of our lives and our thinking are not the reflection of a variation in God. He remains the same unchanging, loving Father of us all."

Sue Reinhardt paused and looked a little embarrassed.

"Well," she apologized, "you didn't come here for a sermon from me."

"We wish you'd go on," I said, daring to speak for everyone there, even Janet not excepted.

"No matter where you are," she continued, and her cheeks wore a flush from the excitement of this giving, "no matter where you are, you are likely to come across faces with that sort of stuffy look that holds back the soul from looking out through the eyes with something to share. Thank goodness, though, you are sure to find other faces so filled with a shining glow that you feel your own heart lightening.

"I sometimes like thinking over the age-long questions," said Sue. " 'Is this an ordered world?' I ask myself. 'Is Someone in wise and loving control? Is He an Almighty Father, caring for me as an individual?' The thought that He is caring for me as personally as though there were no one else in the world is stupendous. But I believe it."

Sue suddenly drew into herself as though she hadn't intended to say so much, and it was Janet who urged her on,

"Well, just the same," objected Janet, "I'd like to know how you got through last night on those ideas."

"Do you really want to know?" Sue said, searching Janet's face quietly. "For one thing I tried to get to sleep by using three of my favorite verses from the Bible, which I've had in my head for years:

> 'He maketh the storm a calm
> So that the waves thereof are still.
> Then are they glad because they are quiet.
> So He bringeth them unto their desired haven.'

and those other familiar ones:

> 'In peace will I both lay me down and sleep, for Thou, Lord, alone makest me to dwell in safety.'

and:

> 'When thou liest down, thou shalt not be afraid;
> Yea, thou shalt lie down and thy sleep shall be sweet.'

You see, nothing can separate us from the love of God, not even painful noises in the night."

"So you slept, did you?" pressed Janet.

"Not too much, Janet, and I agree with you it's hard to go without sleep. Still, they tell us that if we lie quietly, instead of tensely, we do get our night's rest, even if we don't sleep all the time."

"So how lie quietly?" asked Harriet.

Sue hesitated a moment, then smiled.

"There are other verses for that. One is:

'Because He is at my right hand, I shall not be moved.'

And then,

'The peace of God, which passeth all understanding, shall guard your hearts and your thoughts.'

That idea of having my thoughts *guarded* I've always found wonderful. And this:

'Thou wilt keep him in perfect peace whose mind is stayed on thee, because he trusteth in thee.' "

Sue looked at Janet and waited before she went on.

"And there's another thing," she said. "I try to put suffering people into God's care by praying. I think we aren't given needy neighbors so that we may carry them on our backs, but so that we may carry them on wings of prayer. And I do believe in personal prayer as a helpful force. I have faith that, in a way we can't understand, His love is enfolding them and we can trust Him."

"But you hear things just the same," insisted Janet.

"I know it, Janet," Sue agreed, "and I don't suppose I really like it any better than you do."

Then she turned to us three.

"It is true," she admitted, "that our friend is suffering and we know it and it does test our belief in a God of love and mercy. But He will not allow her to have more than she can bear—can bear, that is, in His strength, because the power of God is equal to anything, mysterious though this seems. Through prayer—and this is a wonderful fact—we are able to save our own limited energy and act as channels for God's own spirit, which has no limits."

Sue waited a minute, but we were all so quiet that she dared to continue.

"Harriet asked a while ago how this kind of strain on sympathy can be surmounted, and now I have given you some of my own helps. You see it isn't a question of whether you can stand it, or 'sustain' it, as Janet says. The question is how calmly you can accept it." Here Sue's face grew quite serious. "I see women come here with a tight-lipped will to endure anything and everything. They seem to have steeled themselves to an indifference to even such happiness as they might find, or might give. I do not believe that we can afford to be indifferent here, either to pain or to pleasure. That's why your word *surmount*, Harriet, is so good. You can't meet the problems of old age head-on at your own level. You've got to raise your head above them and, what is more, keep it there. Whoever does that becomes not only a peaceful person, but a useful one.

"It's a good idea," Sue continued, "to learn how to be sincerely sympathetic with a troubled or suffering person while you are with her, but then to drop concern about her completely, *except* in prayer. You can pray such words as 'Be thou a stronghold to the needy in distress,' knowing that at the same time the Lord is *your* stronghold, too. And that familiar affirmation, 'I let go and let God,' doesn't wear out. It can be counted on to relax needless tension and keep us free for service to many who may be around us, to whose happiness we can contribute richly.

"That reminds me," Sue went on, "of eight words that I learned many years ago from a book called *Faith and Health*, by Charles Reynolds Brown. I think it's out of print now. Dr. Brown had himself known a serious nervous breakdown, and from his experience during recovery he had many ideas to share, including his successful use of suggestion." Here Sue opened a book that was on the table beside her.

"He is speaking of 'the Americans who are so restless that even when they sit down they cannot be still, they must rock to and fro as if they were going somewhere.' He goes on, 'Here is a case where suggestion is "indicated," as the physicians say. If there is no organic disease, suggestion will do [this woman] ten times more good than drugs. If she will only say to herself slowly, thoughtfully, expectantly, every night after she gets into bed and every morning before she gets up, three times a day before meals and three times a day after meals, and at intervals of an hour or two during the day—if she will only say to herself these eight words which so many people have found useful, it will do her a world of good. The results may not appear in ten minutes or in a day, but in a surprisingly short time they will work a beneficent change in her whole nervous system. Here are the eight words:

QUIETLY, EASILY,
RESTFULLY, TRUSTFULLY,
PATIENTLY, SERENELY,
PEACEFULLY, JOYOUSLY

" 'If you find yourself talking too loud, moving with jerks, losing your self-control, liable to petulant speech, breaking out in spurts of anger; or if you find yourself constantly out of breath, all unstrung, feeling as if you might fly to pieces, stop right there! Sit down and do your exercises! Say to yourself, either audibly or mentally, "Quietly, easily, restfully, trustfully, patiently, serenely, peacefully, joyously."

" 'You can thus control your own mental states if you set about it in the right way. We are not responsible for the random thoughts which come and go; we are responsible for those which come and settle down to summer and winter with us. As the old proverb had it, "You cannot keep the birds from flying over your head, but you can keep them from building their nests in your hair." You are responsible for those states of mind which you retain and cherish. And where you are convinced that in your own case there is a tendency to be morbid and unwholesome you can, by systematic and persistent suggestion, change all that and make it right.' "

Sue closed her book quietly and waited while we took this in.

"I want to write those eight words down," I said, "so that we all can have them."

"And, oh, sometime," Sue added, "I'll tell you the Four Lines I made up to use while Mr. Reinhardt was in his last illness. For many months I tried to have him feel that I was free from anxiety and strain. I knew that I couldn't fool him, for we had lived together too long. My courage had to be the real thing or he would know it and worry about depending on me."

"Why don't you give us your Four Lines now?" I urged.

Sue leaned back comfortably and said, "Only these simple words:

> Breathe deep of the love of God,
> Be strong by using His power,
> Find joy in high courage and hope,
> And help yourself to peace.

And I mean 'help yourself' in two senses," she explained. "First, that you must do the seeking, for your own sake. Then, that you must help yourself freely, as you help yourself to good food. They say that old ladies are apt to take too shallow breaths. So I breathe slowly and deeply as I go from one line to the next and keep repeating them in my head."

Then Janet spoke again.

"You're lucky," she complained, pinning her eyes on Sue. "You knew all these things before you came here."

It seemed to me at the time that in this very complaint there was a shade of new understanding on Janet's part, almost a bit of surrender.

"Yes, I am lucky," said Sue. Then she added positively, "But they can be learned. When you affirm peaceful, strengthening things to yourself, over and over, it's your own private peace and strength you are building up, and that is something you and no one else can control. When your mind and body are at peace, you have power to surmount an annoyance," she concluded, turning to Harriet, "instead of letting the annoyance surmount you."

Then Sue started having us try her lines. Even Janet

sat there taking deep breaths and saying over the words to herself, however reluctantly. I could see that she felt silly and, too, that she was afraid of letting her stiffened back go, of perhaps yielding to Sue's ideas. Suddenly the whole scene proved too much for Harriet and it was true that we had become pretty solemn. She relieved the tension by bursting into our mood with a hearty laugh.

"Forgive me, but I can't help saying something that flashed into my head, and it's no irreverence to what you've been giving us, Sue," she explained. "But remember, girls, Miss Fulton and gym and deep breathing and how I always had trouble jumping over the big leather horse?"

This must have been a good break, for we all laughed and Sue made a gesture for me to close the transom. Once I was on my feet, it was a signal for us three to leave.

"I must say, Sue," declared Mary, still smiling, "you've been mighty good to let us touch on the homeliest details . . . the homeliest and holiest," she added, putting her hand on Sue's shoulder.

I didn't know how to say my thanks. I looked not at Sue but at Harriet. I thought the frown on her forehead had definitely cleared. As we went out the main door, she spoke.

"What you've got to have is something that makes you livable *and* lovable. That's Sue, and I must say I'd like to own whatever that is in her face. What is it, Mary?"

"Isn't it the very radiance she was talking about?" Mary replied. "But the flick of a button doesn't bring on current like hers. It has to do with all she was telling us about, and more, too."

"If only you could hold it the way she seems to," sighed Harriet as we got into the car. "You wouldn't think," she went on, "three women could go so low and so high as we did in so short a time. Janet certainly meant to let us come to grips with the worst. But did you people notice that she started showing a slight admiration for Sue in spite of herself? Notice I said, 'slight.'"

"I think I begin to know how a reconditioned car must feel," I sighed. "Sue made it sound possible to do those things, to believe those things. I wish I'd begun years ago. Do you suppose it's too late?"

We had halted at a stoplight and Mary turned to me with a look of compassion I shall never forget. I think that her own wholehearted desire to recondition herself gave her an understanding of my anxious little outcry. She must have recognized that life had let her plumb grimmer deeps than either Harriet or I had known. What she said to me was, "No, I don't believe it's too late for any one of us." Then she smiled as she put her foot on the accelerator. "At any rate," she said, "not if time lets us have your Seven Years."

CHAPTER 9

Because of an Air Conditioner

When I was back inside my apartment once more, I made a swift checkup in the hall mirror, remembering the despair in my face after our first visit to The Walden. The change wasn't too great, yet the scared look of a few weeks ago was disappearing. Something new and different was reflected in my eyes. At that moment I felt very humble and I said to myself, "That's Sue for you."

I knew that it was Sue and it was Mary and Harriet, too. And somehow even Janet had had an influence on me this afternoon. Perhaps she did have a long way to go but I felt real warmth toward her as I thought of the start she appeared to be making.

"Perhaps in the end," I smiled, "Janet will be the tortoise who wins out."

As it hadn't seemed convenient for Harriet to have us at Eileen's, we three had held our get-togethers either in my apartment or Mary's house. She had a spacious home which we all knew was too much for her to take care of. A few days after our most recent visit at The Walden, the girls were scheduled to come to me, but Mary telephoned to urge that we must, simply *must,* go to her this time. She believed we'd find her room cooler in the humid weather.

"I haven't said a thing to anybody," she told us at the door, with her forefinger across her lips, "but I've taken a step so drastic that I'd be alarmed, if it hadn't already brought such utter relief."

She pointed to the door into her back living room, which was closed.

"Hear it purr?" she asked and we must have looked puzzled.

"My new air conditioner. Come in!" she said with a flourish.

We went into a room that was restful in its simplicity.

"But it looks so different," exclaimed Harriet. "What-all have you done? Where are . . . where are the *things?*"

Mary's eyes sparkled.

"I don't want to have to leave this big home of mine now," she replied, "not for a thousand reasons. But I decided the only way I could stay was to simplify. It occurred to me that, if I had the comfort of an air conditioner during these dog days, I'd want to spend my time in this one cool, dry room, day and night. So, believe it or not, I've closed off the dining room for active use and the whole of upstairs, except to allow some circulation of air. On the hottest days I can bring my meals in here on my gate-leg table, but come out into the kitchen and you'll see my makeshift dinette. When John was ill, we had a bathroom put in on this floor.

. . . So now I have my little apartment, and it's just as simple as that."

We returned from our little excursion and settled into the refreshing atmosphere.

"See what I've done?" Mary urged. "We had this day-bed here already. I've chosen a few of the easiest chairs from all over the house—the easiest to sit in and the easiest to dust. Then I thought of Sue Reinhardt's single piece of Venetian glass and of what it did for her room. So I made what I called 'sallies of selection' all over the place, trying to pride myself on restraint."

"I had to do that when I went to Eileen's," interrupted Harriet.

Plainly Mary was aware, as I was, that Harriet had gone through a real uprooting, for she went on with a softened voice. "There used to be a host of things in this room that I never used. They were only distractions to the eye and a nuisance to care for. One by one I dismissed most of them, even though some things gave an emotional tug at the time, wanting to be kept. I constantly insisted to myself that this was like weeding a garden and leaving the flowers. And I didn't allow myself to bring anything into the room unless it was needed for easy living.

"Here," she went on, "are the things I'd like to take away with me, wherever I go to live. You can see what they are. The winged chair you're sitting in, Harriet. Radio, of course. A few choice pictures that remind me of this person or that place. That Liberty silk table cover we brought from England. And this was a brass bowl of my mother's. You know what I mean. Nothing too full of sentiment, but all filled with pleasant associations."

Harriet slumped back in her chair and said, "Why, Mary Olmstead, you're ready for The Walden right now."

"That's not so funny as it sounds," smiled Mary. "Remember that reducing my possessions to one roomful at a rest home was one of the dreads I complained about weeks ago? It isn't just the air conditioner that's letting me sleep better. Even in the dark, I can see how peaceful this room looks."

"You're like a snake that has sloughed off his outworn skin," I remarked.

"No wonder the snake glides," Mary said. "It's a wonderful feeling. And now I'm planning to sort and destroy and give away. That's tiring business at best, and I'm convinced that I should do it while I have the strength. I'm never going to heat that second floor in winter again. I'm down to one room . . . and I like it."

"Doesn't it hurt, though, to part with things that had to do with your married life?" asked Harriet knowingly.

"Yes, it did at first," Mary answered, "but what surprises me is that there has come a new intimacy about living that brings John closer. And I mean in a truly lovely way." She hesitated, then said quite simply, "I think I'd like to tell you girls about something I found several years ago."

We both said, "Go on, Mary."

"While John was in the hospital during the last months," she told us, "I kept coming across what I began to call the Essence. And I must say that this discovery was a great comfort to me, and still is. Gradually the associations that at first made me catch my breath came to have a heart-warming reminiscent glow.

"This Essence worked itself increasingly free. It might

Essence

emanate from an object or from something not even tangible—from a strain of music or a flash of humor such as we had enjoyed together. It's hard to describe in words, but it was and is as real to my spirit as John himself was. The Essence seems to burn away grief—grief and regret. It is like an invisible light that gives joy and strength and peace. I can feel that it even brings a special expression to my face."

She stopped and looked around the room.

"Nowadays I can almost summon it at will," she said. "It is definitely of my spiritual world and can pervade a whole day. Don't think I've gone spiritualistic, not in the usual sense," she warned us.

"You must be receptive, though," I suggested. "It must be an attitude of your mind that catches this . . . this Essence. I suppose we can squeeze a freshness out of anything, if we're ready."

"Well, what I'm coming to is this," Mary went on. "I'm trying to train myself to know that this Essence will be mine even in a rest home—that when my world comes down to little things, little events, and perhaps somewhat small people, there will still be this Essence that is the very largeness of my life."

"Perhaps that's the trouble with Janet Coombs," said Harriet, "she's never found Essence enough, if any." Then she went on, "We haven't even mentioned our visit to The Walden the other day. Sue surely gave me a purging."

"Then you're satisfied, Harriet," I asked, "that we have really faced things, which was what you ordered long ago?"

"I wouldn't *not* have done it for anything," Harriet said and I felt something more coming. "Sue left me so dissatisfied with myself that I'm going to confess to you what's happened. All along, I've been hoping to jump in and sink or swim when a change has to come. But now I've decided to learn to float, instead, and I've been trying it out at Eileen's."

Harriet looked a little surprised at herself, but she went on, "I'll tell you the simple truth. Sue has begun to change me. I take the confusion at Eileen's more easily. I see her make mistakes—or what I think are mistakes—and don't have to bite my tongue to keep still. I float. And this morning I even told Tom a white lie, to make him feel comfortable. I said I didn't hear them come in last night. You see, they don't use me for a baby-sitter any more, so I was in bed, and of course I did hear the car, but I didn't let it bother me. Tom and Eileen seem so much more considerate in a number of ways recently."

I wanted to suggest, "Couldn't it be the change in you that's inviting a change in them?" But I didn't. I saw that Harriet had more to let out.

"I've been looking at them both and at the children in a new light, a light that left me as much as possible out of their picture. I've been trying every day not to edge into their lives, but to be a sort of good-natured boarder without interfering fingers. Believe me, I found I had been trying to rule that roost the way I used to rule the schoolroom. I spoke hastily when I didn't mean anything by it. I do really love the whole household, but I must have been playing in an off key."

I couldn't help noticing a new warmth in Harriet's face, as she went on, "This is the kind of thing that's happening. Yesterday at breakfast Tom noticed when I was ready for more coffee without my asking. Then he said, 'Seems to me you do a lot to help Eileen.' I knew that she must have talked with Tom because he added, 'Seems to me lately you fit right in.' It was that word 'lately' that paid for the effort I'm making.

"Don't think I'm too good all of a sudden, girls," she went on, "but I began to recognize that I'd been harboring a feeling of being abused by Eileen, in fact, by all of them. Imagine my carrying that sort of idea to a Walden! Why, I could rouse up notions that everyone from one end to the other of the whole institution was 'against' me. I began a little cautiously to notice and even speak of Eileen's thoughtfulness toward me and to the children, and now you ought to see what she's doing for me. She may be my daughter, but Eileen's quite a girl."

Harriet stopped, and it was clear that she had no more to say.

"If you're through," I ventured, and she nodded for me to go ahead, "I have a confession of my own about what Sue did for me the last time. I went home and decided to take one of my failings in hand, especially after what Sue had said about rising above noise. That's one of my worst points. I positively sink under sounds. To use Harriet's expression, I decided I had to learn to float on top of noise and I came against a test right away. Within the first twenty-four hours, everything! The young child across the way from our apartment house had two violent crying spells, one at midnight, one in the very early hours."

"And did you try Sue's Four Lines?" probed Harriet.

"You're not going to catch me there. I did, and they helped," I answered her. "But the next day, believe it or not, hear this list: power mower on our lawn, the highway department with a buzz saw on the big tree in front of the house, a paint sprayer next door, and don't let me forget the squirrel that scolded the cat and the bluejay for what seemed like hours. . . . One thing that makes me think I may have improved a little is that just now I didn't say to you that the squirrel 'scolded and scolded and scolded.' I said only one 'scolded.' For me that is a remarkable change, whether you know it or not!"

Harriet stretched her feet forward on the rug with an air of real relaxation.

"Do you see what's happening, girls?" she asked. "It seems that most of the failings of old age don't *start* in rest homes. Janet Coombs, if you remember, never could over-look slights, or what she thought were slights, not even when she was a girl. And yesterday I thought about this when I met a middle-ager who never can avoid gossiping, especially about mean things. She'll make a humdinger when she gets to a Walden, if she doesn't watch out now. But there I am, wanting to make other people over. One thing's sure, you won't be able to change other people, not unless you live it out the way Sue does. You can't be the kind of person who goes up to someone else and says, 'I think I ought to tell you' or 'I think you'd want me to tell you' this, that, or the other failing. Women don't enter a home, you can better believe, for the purpose of having their characters made over, even though Sue says they can and do change."

"There's one thing I've been saying to myself," I interrupted. "Wherever I go, the first person I'll find there will be myself."

"That's what I mean," said Harriet, "and you might as well be able to enjoy meeting yourself. That's where I'm beginning—with myself—and it's a large order."

"I recall saying the other day," I remarked, "that I felt like a reconditioned car after seeing Sue Reinhardt. Today I'm going to say instead that Sue is working on me like an air conditioner. Thanks for the idea, Mary."

CHAPTER 10

Personnel and Other Friends

Now that we three had settled into trying to make ourselves over, we seemed unwilling to meet without Sue. Janet, too, had become somehow indispensable to our sessions. Sue must have taken pleasure in helping us. In fact, she was so intent on sharing her observations that we had come to think *with* her instead of *about* her, as at first. We liked seeing our future through her eyes, and Sue must have felt this.

On our next visit, Harriet didn't even wait to get seated before she began probing.

"So what's on the boards today, Sue?" she inquired.

"People," said Sue.

"So what about people?" I asked.

"Since you were here," Sue answered, "several things have happened to make me think about the personnel and other friends here. I mean my relationship to them. I've been trying to keep one question active in my mind: 'How easy can I make it for the personnel?' "

"I don't believe that's new to you," observed Mary.

"You're all right in your relationship with us, Sue," agreed Harriet, and Sue smiled.

"Of course, the Golden Rule is old stuff," she began, "but I sometimes think if only every guest here would speak to the staff as she would that the staff should speak unto her. . . ."

She knew that she didn't need to finish the sentence.

"What are the meanest things guests can do?" urged Harriet, looking a bit sheepish for asking.

"Well, very little things can be mighty mean," Sue said. "For instance, there's a woman who is really very nice in lots of ways, but she insists on having the waitress take back her muffins to the kitchen if they aren't slightly burned —yes, burned. That's the only way she can eat them, she says."

Sue paused and seemed pleased that none of us looked amused.

"Of course," she went on, "that is an extreme, but it doesn't take many idiosyncrasies to wilt a waitress and a kitchen. And, that, in turn, wilts Miss Holden, or it would if she didn't have such infinite patience with us."

I saw Janet struggling; then she came out with it.

"But you can't help being somewhat different, can you?" she asked. "Not, that is, if you're going to preserve your individuality."

Mary gave a quick glance at Sue. We all waited for her to toss that one back, but she simply bypassed it.

"You know the little woman with the crutches," she said to Janet and then turned to the rest of us to explain. "This lady is really deformed and, I think, in considerable pain.

But she sails around here with so many agreeable words
and nods to guests and staff alike that I, for one, always hope
I'll meet her in the hall. What do you think her secret is,
Janet?" Sue pressed, but Janet looked puzzled at being
consulted and Sue answered her own question.

"For instance, she always says pleasant things as though
she meant them. Her *please* and *thank you* ring more true
than those words from almost anyone I've known. It may
be thanks for nothing more than that someone picks up a
letter she has dropped, but her heart is in that gratitude.
It's the same way, if you notice," and here Sue turned
definitely to Janet again, "when she says 'I'm sorry' or 'excuse
me.' Then, too, she always remembers to call people by
name. The staff just love her because she mentions what
might seem like trifles, such as something one of them did
to make her night's sleep more comfortable. And she will
remember a kindness for days and speak of it as one fingers
over a keepsake."

"That kind of appreciation is a gift," Harriet remarked,
but Sue didn't let it go at that.

"Yes, it is, but it's a gift that can be cultivated," she
said. "Once in a while by contrast you see someone who is
demanding the best and the best only in every detail of
service, who is everlastingly watching for little *wrongs* and
forgets to note little *rights*. It may be necessary for a helper
to do things her own way, instead of yours, in the course of
her routine. And you must be game for accepting this, if
you want to make it easy for the personnel. Only today I
heard a guest exclaim, 'What in the world do they think
I'm *paying* for . . . *anyhow?*' "

Sue relaxed consciously and then added, "She really

didn't need the 'anyhow.' The way she raised her voice was enough!"

"I don't care," said Janet, completely missing the point, "I wish that cleaning woman they've hired recently would mop under the bureau."

I believe this was the only time I had heard Sue chide Janet, yet she did it with an unmistakable friendliness in her warm brown eyes.

"Don't you think," she said, "there are some things you have to close your eyes to, at times? Miss Holden really means to keep our rooms clean."

Sue looked around at all of us and then started to smile.

"I guess I'll have to tell you what happened to me the other day," she went on. "I had a slight cold and that meant dinner on a tray in my room. The little attendant who brought it to me is in love and she forgot to put either a knife or a fork by my plate. But there *was* a spoon. I started to push my buzzer. Then I recalled the frantic jerk I had seen someone give to her bell for a slight mistake, and besides I knew that Elsa was needed in the dining room. So I decided to see what I could do with only a spoon. It went very well and when she came for the empty tray I told her how I got along and what a laugh she had."

I doubt whether Sue knew that she was showing us her own graciousness. With her this was just a joke. Needless to say, Janet couldn't let this ride.

"All the same," she said, "they ought to do things right."

"But when you come to think about it, Janet," I had to say, "it must be a tremendous job to run a place like this. I mean with women being so quick-spoken and jealous and resentful and everything. I marvel that anyone ever takes it on. There must be a lot more to it than providing meals and seeing that rooms are cared for, mustn't there?"

I found myself turning to Sue for an answer.

"You're hitting something I often think of," she said, "when someone here resents the idea that maybe we are thought to be in our 'second childhood.' It is up to us to live those two words down by not expecting special attention."

"Like teacher's pet," put in Harriet.

"Yes," said Sue, "when we are supposed to have 'put away childish things.' One of you just spoke about taking on a job like this institution. I sometimes wonder why anyone, from the Board of Directors (and we have some mighty nice ones) down to the choreman who is called on to quiet a sputtering radiator (while the occupant of the room herself sputters)—why the whole sequence of them is willing to do it. There must be a special spirit of devotion to such a calling, for they surely do know great stress and strain. And they take a chance on our increasing frailty and on our dispositions."

Sue weighed her words a moment and then went on, but she appeared to avoid looking at Janet as she spoke.

"Of course, impatience is about the best way of clogging the works here. There often is waiting. It seems as if a helper could and should come to one's side at the moment of call, and I *don't* believe that *neglect* of any kind should be condoned. But even the most conscientious attendant can be pulled a dozen ways at once. Just as in any family, there are times when everybody seems to want Mother, when everything is equally important, and Mother can hardly think what to do first.

Patience

"This," Sue went on, "is a very hard fact to accept in a home, because you have been able to get things done or else to do them yourself. Now you have to fall into line, and this is often a real waiting line. You have to 'let patience have its perfect work,' knowing that nothing can wear down you or others much more than the loss of your patience. You have only to watch the woman who bursts out with the words, 'Sometimes I get so ex-*as*-perated!' Even though she finds her patience again, the day is never what it might have been for anyone concerned."

"People like that find it difficult to apologize, too, don't they?" asked Mary.

"They are the kind," Sue said, "who seem unable to dismiss any injury, real or imagined. Perhaps they turn cool —deadly cool—as a substitute for apologizing, withdrawing into their pride. This is the time to stir in a bit of humor, if possible, but that is very hard to do in the face of tension, even though it's worth a mint to everyone, if it is done right.

wheel

"After all," she went on, "The Walden is like a great wheel that must turn smoothly for the good of all concerned. To me it seems as if each guest, each administrator and helper of any sort—every single one of us—is a spoke set into this revolving wheel. And on the steadiness of both the served and the serving depends the smooth turning. If I fail here or there, I may be the one to make the wheel creak. As someone wrote, 'It is not the number of revolutions but the friction that wears the wheel.' "

"A rest home," said Harriet, "is really just a group of strangers who find themselves under one roof."

"Yes," said Sue, "just stop to consider the psychological task of gathering into one home atmosphere a collection of

aging people. No wonder it is both our duty and pleasure
to lighten each other's loads and to think out what care *we*
can take of the *staff*. I mean by being on the alert to ap-
preciate, to save them unnecessary work, to help them in
little ways when we can, like being prompt at meals and
being willing to sit where our hostess places us. The more
cooperation we can show, the more sense of belonging and
of being useful we can gain.

Staff

"The cook," she went on, "adores having a special word
of commendation sent out to the kitchen. And I've seen a
'thank you' whispered with the grace of a benediction by a
very sick woman, who had scarcely strength of mind or body
to say even that. A single word can freshen the energy of a
helper in her daily, or nightly, round."

Cook

"You have to respect the dignity of their work, don't
you?" suggested Mary.

"The dignity and the difficulty," said Sue. "Of course,
in a community like this many kinds of mistakes are bound
to be made by human hands and heads. Sometimes the
young helper who seems tired may have just done a service
in the room of someone who was bulging with complaints—
complaints of the weather, of the administration in Wash-
ington, of the egg she had for breakfast, of Russia, of the
way she didn't sleep, and of the noise of her neighbor's radio.
To be sure, there are helpers who want to tell their own
troubles too freely to everyone. But perhaps that doesn't do
us much harm. I have a theory that as soon as I shut myself
from the ills and anxieties of others, my own ills and anxieties are certain to close in around me."

"When John was in the hospital," Mary said, "I found
it really did *me* good to give appreciation to the doctors,

the nurses, and to others who were trying to help him. I still remember one woman who made John's scrambled eggs just the way he liked them." Mary paused and then added, "And do you know, Sue, I never entered or left that corridor without a special prayer of thanks to God for their ministration and a petition for His blessing on every one of them."

None of us spoke for a few moments. The windows were open and balmy air was drifting quietly in.

"Yes," said Sue, "in a hospital or in a home like this, the personnel and the other patients or guests become our friends, if we go halfway. We have to become a sort of family because we share so many minutes of the day, minutes often filled with the prosaic, mechanical, and realistic means of living. Nowadays we see in print and hear on the radio many discussions of human relations. Human relations," repeated Sue with a flicker of amusement, "are what we have here at The Walden."

"Aren't a lot of people wary or shy about starting friendships in a place like this?" I asked.

"They are," said Sue, "but a little outgoing warmth thaws a cool exterior and uncovers a real longing for friendliness. If you take the first step across the dividing line because you want the place to be one of good comradeship, the second step may be taken by the other person. It is true that you may have to unbend to give; but, strangely enough, some people have to unbend to receive. Yet I have seen neighbors here who at first felt miles apart, but who shortly became friends. One thoughtful act or word does not stop with its little moment. It creates an atmosphere that lasts, and a heart once warmed is never quite so cold again. I told a really lovely person who came to The Walden that she ought not to wait to speak to people just because she was new.

" 'We need you,' I said to her, 'and if you feel drawn toward anyone here, do be the one to start,' and she surely knew how to make the advance."

"We all need to feel significant in the lives of others, isn't that part of it, Sue?" I asked. "When I enter a home, if I do, I'm going to bank on meeting someone who will become an intimate friend. I've never lived anywhere without being lucky enough to find at least one especially congenial person, who stood out in a delightful way. I was thinking over a list of them in my head only last night, and the accumulation has been wonderful. They always seemed to pop up whenever and wherever I wanted them."

"That means the need was mutual," observed Mary.

"Sometimes a truly great friendship," said Sue, "is formed here. It's never too late to come across a new friend, and we never stop craving to love and be loved. Loneliness is lovelessness. And," she advised, "it doesn't do to eye your daily companions with a studied appraisal. Snap judgment, too, may get fooled. You can't be what is called 'choosy.' It isn't like the days when you selected your list of guests for a supper party in your own home. Here you have to lay hold on a different kind of sociability. But you can still give yourself in gracious conversation and courtesy.

"I suppose you all know," Sue went on, "that it is a pipe dream to believe that your old friends will come to see you often, even though you have lived in the same general neighborhood before. You girls have been wonderful and it has meant a lot to me and to Janet. But too many of our contemporaries in the early seventies and on up are in somewhat the same fix and they can't very well get to see us any more than we can get to see them. Younger friends are refreshing, but they are busied with their own lives, just as we used to be.

"What I'm trying to say is that we have to become agreeably absorbed in those who are near us. Don't for a minute let them tell you that aging people aren't interesting, thoughtful, and even merry. *We can be.* I know that some women are more compatible to me than others, and I know that even I have traits that may not attract some people," Sue smiled. "But I have a motto for my own use: If someone rubs you the wrong way, try rubbing her the right way."

Janet had been pretty quiet but now she spoke.

"I can stand anything but getting stuck with someone who talks and talks and talks and tells the same story over and over," she complained. "You know who I mean, Sue."

Sue laughed and said, "Perhaps you mean me, Janet?"

"If they were all like Mrs. Royce, I wouldn't mind," said Janet.

"That would be something," agreed Sue. Then, turning to us, she explained, "Mrs. Royce is a woman over ninety here who has no end of self-reliance and a very gay heart. She was a musician and always studies the advance radio programs so that she can tell the rest of us what is coming in the way of good music. She has lived a troubled life with nothing short of valor. You can see that in her face, can't you, Janet?" Sue asked.

Janet answered nothing to the contrary.

"A certain young professor is helping Mrs. Royce," Sue went on, "in the editing of unpublished manuscripts and letters that her author-husband left. Often he brings his young son, simply because Pete likes to come. And Mrs. Royce lets the boy set up her low folding table and go to a special drawer to get the crayons and drawing book which she keeps there to amuse him while his father is conferring with her. Sometimes Pete drops in here to show me what he has accomplished. We don't see children very often," said Sue a trifle wistfully.

Then she continued, "I think I spoke of being too 'choosy.' A new sense of values comes over you when you live in a rest home, and particularly a new sense of time. For years you will have been useful by the clock. Now time takes on an unhurried way. To keep your self-confidence you like to feel some pressure, but this new pressure isn't like the old scheduled demand. It is a voluntary, quiet discipline of thoughtfulness of others that should be both spontaneous and elastic. In every sense, it gives."

Here Mary interrupted. "You mean that time isn't important—only kindness gets to be important?"

"That's it," said Sue, "and it applies to making friends. You no longer calculate that this person or that one is 'worth your time.' The daily question is, where are you clever enough to detect some little need that can be met without calculating either the cost or the gain to yourself? This is genuine friendliness."

"That's what Shakespeare meant by 'grace and good disposition,'" said Harriet, and I realized that we had not yet talked over this familiar quotation with Sue.

Sue nodded and then looked at me.

"This is the first day I've felt as though I were truly inviting you three to look forward to the coming segment of your living. You know its difficulties now. We've dealt with many of them together. But obviously friendship is one of the things that will do most to make you contented. Friends help you make a gallant approach to increasing age so that you never let it catch up with you."

"But everybody isn't built like you, Sue," objected Harriet. "Couldn't some people be officious in this giving-yourself program?"

It seemed as though Harriet was definitely letting herself in for some sort of reproof. But not from Sue.

Instead she looked at Janet and said, "You spoke a few minutes ago about some women who tell the same story over and over, Janet. It is hard, especially when you're seated beside an overly talkative person at table and she has you cornered. But a woman like that enjoys someone to talk *to* more than someone to talk *with,* and you may as well relax and give in to her. There just are people who feel lonely and want to be listened to above everything. If you realize that, you can stand talk of physical ailments and reminiscences of all sorts without its wearing on you."

A little mischief came into Sue's eye as she went on, "If you begin to get impossibly bored, there is a technique of listening with only half an ear."

"What do you mean by 'technique'?" probed Janet. "Mrs. Randall certainly bores me, if only to look at her."

Sue seemed a little unwilling to give away her secrets to Janet, but she did say, "Well, it's gracious to ask a question or make a comment now and then—to show that you are there. I suppose it may be naughty of me," she suggested, "but I sometimes find I haven't been listening too closely and then I ask, 'How long ago was that?'"

CHAPTER 11

We See Ourselves

A few days later I had an errand near The Walden and was glad enough to visit alone with Sue. When I saw the quick sparkle in her eyes at my surprising her, I decided to do it oftener. With that keen understanding of hers, she seemed to know that I had come for some special reason, and I had.

"Sue," I began right off, "I told Mary and Harriet that you are working on me like an air conditioner. And I want to talk with you specifically about this grace-and-good-disposition business—specifically with reference to myself, I mean. I'm still concerned about my future, particularly as to whether I have what it takes. I think I need a sort of checklist from you. That is, I want you to name over the most troublesome traits I should be trying to root out of my own life right now, in preparation. I honestly want to smooth off my sharp edges."

"I'm not worried about you," Sue said, but we did mention a lot of little annoying things and of course I took shorthand notes. I noticed that she kept saying, "You have to avoid this, or to be sure to do that," as our list accumulated. When we had gone about so far, I said, "Sue, this is all too good for Harriet and Mary to miss. I'm going to type out these topics and call a meeting of us all, including Janet, if she wants to come. And then let's have a character buzz."

"A personality buzz," Sue amended. "The other three will have things to contribute, and I'll be thinking. We could almost get up a little handbook of *Shalt's* and *Shalt-Not's*. I need a check-up myself."

The next day I told Mary and Harriet over the telephone how Sue and I had happened to make up an agenda for discussion. When I relayed some of Sue's illustrations from real life, they were intrigued, and Harriet started on some observations of her own, but I told her to hold them.

On the way over I said by way of warning, "We aren't in for entertainment today, you know. It may be a stiff session. Sue and I are resolved to see ourselves as others might see us."

That was what we all agreed on, when we had taken our usual places in Sue's little room.

"I found ten good solid topics in my notes," I said to Sue, "and I made them up to read like the Ten Commandments, in a way."

"I suppose," put in Harriet, "if I kept every one of these, I'd be wafted straight to heaven without even a stopover at The Walden!"

After a quick smile at this Harriet-like remark, I started.

"First: Thou shalt speak agreeable words," I read. "You tell them, Sue, what you said about this the other day."

"There are many little hurts," she began after a pause, "that can come from the spoken word. I think that people's tongues make the most trouble here, don't you, Janet?"

Janet squirmed a trifle and then said, "The way Mrs. O. spoke to me this noon, you mean? You must have heard her."

Sue took the reins again. As she started, I saw Harriet bend forward in her chair as though the way Sue managed Janet was an eye-opener.

"Of course," Sue was saying, "these little things that sometimes seem deliberately spiteful are often said by women who feel insecure and are afraid they aren't duly regarded by others. Take the woman who seeks importance by stating, 'I don't want to raise an issue, but . . .' It's plain that she definitely does want to raise an issue for some reason that may be deep inside her."

"And she intends to go ahead with it, too," put in Harriet. "She hasn't a notion of holding back to save someone's feelings."

"But aren't some poeple built that way?" I asked, knowing this was a silly question for which Sue would have an answer, but she was wise enough to pass over it.

"One key to agreeable speech," she said, "is in the verse, 'Let not thy heart be hasty to utter anything.' Notice that word *heart*. If your heart isn't hasty, your lips can't be. Luckily, many spontaneous words are pleasant. Yet since you were here," she went on, looking at me, "I've jotted down some sample phrases that often come too easily to the tongue. I say some of them myself," she confessed.

Sue gave a slightly playful glance at Janet and added, "You must have heard me use them, especially when I first came to The Walden."

I thought Janet's face looked puzzled and a little fearful of what might be coming.

"In a close-knit group like this," Sue explained, "you notice that sharp remarks can prick both ways. I think it was Phillips Brooks who wrote in one of his prayers, 'Preserve me from minding little stings—and from giving them.'"

Sue smiled as she took up her list and said, "Interrupt me when you want to. You'll all recognize these troublemakers: 'I don't see why you took it on yourself. . . .'; 'How could I help being annoyed? Wouldn't you have been?'; 'After all, she gave me plenty of provocation.'"

Mary spoke here.

"Those two words, *after all,*" she said, "aren't so bad in themselves; they are like *but, of course,* and *naturally.* It's the tone of voice that can carry the harm, isn't it?"

"I know exactly what you mean," broke in Harriet and she proceeded to give us an illustration: "*Nat*-urally. *Nat*urally *not!*"

Her inflection and accent were so perfect that even Janet found herself laughing.

"If you wish to know why I am so good at that," Harriet added, I'll tell you. That's one of my own words and it can be mighty mean."

"You're right about the tone of voice," I put in. "There's a saucy uptilt that can simply deflate another person. There is also that cold, dead silence after something has been said—a silence that conveys utter scorn."

"And a coldness as hot as pepper," suggested Harriet. "And here's another thing. I hate to have a woman seem to be listening agreeably to me, yet really making a criticism by forcing a little question-mark cough all the while I'm talking, to show that she disagrees."

"You'd better get on with your list of red flags," I said to Sue.

She read again from her paper: " 'May I suggest that another time. . . .'; 'Well, have it your own way. . . .'; 'You can always depend on me to say exactly what I think.' "

Here Harriet raised her hand like a schoolgirl.

"I," she said, "can't stand it to have anyone start out with, 'All I can say is . . .' "

Then Sue made an admission: "I've always had to fight the habit of hanging onto something controversial. I used to like to get it settled my way and, if I couldn't, I'd go over and over it afterwards to myself. Things won't slide off your back unless you give them a slight push. And giving in doesn't mean that you surrender your personality, either."

It was difficult for me to believe that Sue had had to fight disagreeable traits, like the rest of us. Clearly she had come through only with a struggle. Perhaps that was why she was so ready to help. She closed off this topic now with a gesture for me to go on.

"Second: Thou shalt both apologize and forgive wholeheartedly," I read from my paper. "You remember, Sue."

"Oh, yes. You and I," started Sue, "were speaking of how an apology that isn't meant, or has a little tag hanging to it, is worse than no apology at all."

"What do you mean by 'little tag'?" asked Harriet.

"I mean," said Sue, "when you say, 'Of course I'm sorry . . . but I wouldn't have done it if I hadn't felt justified.' Or perhaps, 'I'm sorry I spoke the way I did . . . but she was the one who began it.' You can't be truly sorry unless you forgive and want to be forgiven. If you have made a mistake or misjudgment, or have unintentionally hurt someone, you can't afford to be proud about repenting. Misunderstandings grow. It pays to make amends soon and in a way that helps both sides forget."

"Then there was the other sort of apology, Sue," I said, "the mention of a handicap."

As Sue spoke, she looked away from Janet.

"If you are somewhat crippled so that you can't readily rise to greet another person, you don't need to apologize. The reason will be plain enough. An apology of that kind may actually come from self-pity, which in turn urges pity from another."

This must have hit the mark because Janet asked, "Well, what else can a woman like that do?"

Although Sue hesitated, I felt that she had a measure of confidence in Janet.

"The handicapped woman," she said, "can show immediate interest in the other person by some sincere, pleasant remark. Perhaps about a becoming dress or hat . . . well, any subject that takes them both away from the handicap, I'd say. Notice, Janet, how Mrs. Bradford never says that she can't hear what's going on because her hearing aid doesn't work too well in group conversation? She either lets the talk pass by her or finds some friend afterward who is only too glad to give her a résumé. There's no stigma to wearing a hearing aid, by the way. It is a cane for the ears just as glasses are a cane for the eyes."

"A minute ago, you spoke of not being wholeheartedly sorry unless you forgive and want to be forgiven," I said to Sue, but Mary broke in.

"That's true at any age," she said. "It begins when we're children."

"Another way of stating," remarked Harriet, "that we are taking our prep course for a Walden during all the years that have gone before!"

Sue smiled her assent and took up the topic once more.

"These so-called 'injuries' to our feelings, when they do occur," she observed, "are hard for most human beings to overlook. And some women are so unbending that you can scarcely pry forgiveness out of them. There's a wide difference between the woman who says, 'I can *never* forgive her for the time when she . . .' and the 'seventy-times-seven' forgiving. *Never* is a terribly binding word. What if it does take elasticity to yield a little and then even a little more? The inner peace you gain when you've been willing to forgive is like a sea breeze on a humid summer day."

"People don't really 'lose face' by saying they're sorry," put in Mary.

"You're right," Sue agreed. "And it never pays to harbor a grudge, especially under a roof like this."

"I think," said Mary, "that between the lines of all this there must be a mutual spirit of 'let's not allow this kind of misunderstanding to happen again, either going or coming.' And it is certainly a good thing not to go over the details of an 'incident'—or as some call it, 'that unfortunate incident'—with the other person in an effort to 'set her right.' John always patched up our differences with the old words, 'let bygones be bygones.' "

"It's happening here," I said to myself, "the very way Sue thought it would—everyone contributing from experience."

"I'll tell you something I loathe having said to me," Harriet told us. " 'I trust you won't get so excited another time.' It never smooths my feathers down, not a little bit."

"Don't most of us depend on some physical activity to smooth down our feathers, Harriet?" I asked, but I turned to Sue with a second question. "When I get to the place where I can't work off something I ought to forget by waxing the floors or washing my hair—well, Sue, how about it then?"

"There is a substitute for those more vigorous outlets of younger days that you mention," she said, "but it is *very* passive. To help work off a 'hurt' you truly want to overlook, there's nothing surer than a swift act of prayer, a prayer straight from the heart, saying, 'I know that she didn't mean anything.'

"Such prayers," she went on, "are something like clothespins that hang grievances out to air and sun. Fresh thinking and faith in your fellow man blow through everything with a sort of airy grace."

Harriet raised both arms and folded her hands behind her head, leaning back in deep thought. We slipped into one of those silences that often followed Sue's quiet solutions.

But it was right here that Sue burst out, and I shall always remember this.

"Girls," she said earnestly, "you're letting me do a lot of very high-sounding talking, it seems to me. Every time you've come, I've kept picturing the perfect rest-home guest. Yet believe me, I don't begin to live up to all this—not by a long shot. I know it and anyone here would tell you so. I quibble and lose my patience and get bored. But I'm not proud of it. That isn't the way I really want to be. I'm working at something different. And this goes for everything I've said whenever you've been in this room. The thing of it is, I guess I just can't help thinking about what The Walden could be."

I knew that from then on I would always feel closer to Sue—that we all would. Now we could follow along with anything she wanted to share. When I felt that we were ready to go on, I read, "Third: Thou shalt avoid complaining. I recall your advice, Sue, that when someone asks, 'How do you do?' or 'How are you today?' you shouldn't answer that you 'really have no complaints to make,' in a tone of voice that implies you're hiding something pretty pathetic."

"If you mean a growl, you might as well let it out," Harriet said, but Sue checked her gently.

"The point is not to mean a growl," she laughed. "Repressed growls get taken out on someone or other sooner or later, if it's only on yourself, don't you think?"

"Too often," Mary remarked, "when you ask a person how she is, merely to pass the time of day, you start an awful flow of symptoms—that terrible night's sleep and all the rest of it."

"I know," said Harriet, "people like that can more than buttonhole you, to pour out their troubles." After a moment she added thoughtfully, "I wonder whether I don't do that sometimes . . . with Eileen."

"While John was ill," said Mary, "it used to surprise me to have certain visitors come to unload their difficulties. John would take it agreeably enough, but for his own way of thinking he liked to quote, 'Who am I to complain, who have not ceased to wonder?'"

Sue nodded her head at Mary and then took another tack.

"Of course," she said, "in an institution there is a tendency for women to gather in knots to 'crab' about seeming shortcomings, and this can be like the proverbial summer inn where idle complaints monopolize conversation."

"Sometimes you get caught in a group that's doing that," said Janet, and her words seemed a complaint in themselves.

Sue hesitated, cautious about preaching to Janet.

Then she asked, "Isn't that the time to try *your* hand at giving the talk a smooth turn to things you think are right? I knew a woman with a light touch who did this so naturally that the tension was eased for the whole circle."

"Doesn't everyone here fuss about the weather, simply to have something to talk about?" I asked. "Yet of course you don't have to go out to battle with either hot or cold."

Sue smiled at this and said, "But some women do battle with weather even before it comes. They listen to the forecasts and dote on threatening us all with deep snow or a heat wave. Only this morning I overheard someone saying, 'The sunshine is what I miss. We've had so many gloomy days in succession.'"

"Well, they have been gloomy," put in Janet. "I don't like them either."

Then Harriet spoke.

"Perhaps I've told you all that I boarded around a lot when I was teaching, and the way people griped about food always got me down. I don't condone serving poor food, but women can be so sharp and picayune. I can still hear

the stern way boarders spoke to the waitresses—like this:
'You know I *never* take gravy.'

" 'Oh, you didn't *tell* me it would have chocolate sauce.'

" 'I never *can* eat my meat rare like that.'

" 'But you forgot that I *always* have to have thus-and-so.' "

Sue smiled knowingly, then said quickly: "The kitchen here does cater to individuals, if they have real dietary needs. I don't think that sentences like those you quote, Harriet, are in themselves so troublesome to the waitress. It's the way they are snapped out, usually with self-importance."

"Is that all for the topic about complaining?" I asked, looking around the group.

"Possibly one more thing," Sue said. "I think it is only fair for us not to stack up complaints to tell to callers who are good enough to come in from the outside, or to Miss Holden either. It's too easy to become worried over mere trifles."

Plainly the point was not lost on Janet, for she said with her usual ready application to someone else, "I know one room where Miss Holden must get an earful."

Here I thought I'd better push on, and I read, "Fourth: Thou shalt be thoughtful of others. That one covers almost too much. You start us off, Sue."

"I'm thinking first," she said, "about common courtesies, as described in the Book of Isaiah: 'They help every one his neighbor, and every one saith to his brother, Be of good courage.' "

"I wish Miss Bardwell would say 'please' just once when she wants the sugar passed," said Janet.

I wondered whether Sue would let her get away with that, and she did come back, but with a smile.

"Why don't you try noticing when her tea arrives and pass the sugar before she has to ask?" suggested Sue. "You might get a surprise 'Thanks.' "

"I might—and then again I mightn't," muttered Janet, but Sue pretended not to hear.

"I shall never forget when Mrs. Salter came here," Sue went on. "Plainly she was more in want of security than many. As some of us became aware of this, we ourselves gained security by working to make her feel wanted and loved. This can be done in very small ways," she said with assurance.

"Like what?" asked Harriet.

Quite unexpectedly, Janet answered this.

"You do things yourself, Sue," she said with considerable spontaneity. "You write notes for Mrs. Thompson and I've seen you reading her mail to her."

"I feel sorry for Mrs. Thompson," Sue said, "because some of the guests so obviously show their envy of her beautiful clothes, even though they must know that she can't half see to enjoy them."

"Well, it doesn't seem quite fair she should have a wardrobe like that," said Janet, springing back into her usual self.

"But," said Sue, "her clothes are actually relics of better days. She can't afford to buy anything simple now; she has to wear out what she has."

Mary must have sensed that Sue brought Janet up a little short, so she put in a gentle word.

"That dress you have on yourself, Janet," Mary said,

"looks very nice to me. I noticed it when you came into the room."

Janet melted to this, and I thought, "How little it takes."

"I hoped you would," she said in a voice that she had somehow concealed from us.

I waited a moment in this surprise atmosphere of Janet's own making. Then I read: "Fifth: Thou shalt not be a tale-bearer."

"Do you mean not to gossip?" asked Mary. "I'm absolutely with you on that. I always think of it as a ghost ready to haunt any group of women, and it works special harm as we grow older. It's a ghost that can stay around in the air indefinitely when people aren't alert enough to lay it quickly."

"That's all some people can ever do," said Janet, "gossip, that is. They try digging into everyone's past on purpose to make up stories."

"I like to think of us all as making a new start here," Sue said, "cleared of any past mistakes or misfortune. One of the oldest women here is a wonder about being unwilling even to *hear* tales. In front of gossip I tell her, she keeps not only a poker face but poker ears. If anything idle does come to her, she never passes it on to gratify the curiosity of others. And she never exaggerates just to get attention. You can say of her truly that she would never 'take up a false report.'"

"I'll tell you what I don't like," offered Janet. "I don't like the way Miss Hastings has of lifting her eyebrows and giving her shoulders a shrug. She as much as says she knows something critical that the rest of us aren't in on."

Mary looked at Janet with understanding.

"Yes," she said, "that kind of thing cuts almost worse than words into someone's reputation. We ought to add a fourth monkey to the three that 'see no evil, hear no evil, speak no evil.' Perhaps 'shrug no evil.'"

Then she went on slowly: "I think it takes real compassion not to gossip about others. A certain kind of generous thinking, of magnanimity. Magnanimity and fortitude were two of John's favorite words."

CHAPTER 12

There's More to It

That was one of the days when Miss Holden provided coffee and homemade cookies for us in the dining room. We were all glad to take a little break. When we got back to Sue's room, I began once more.

"This," I said, "brings us to Number Six: Thou shalt exert self-control," and I turned to Sue.

"When age slows down our bodies," she began, "we should put the brakes on our emotions more than ever. The childish tantrum of an old lady is not a pretty thing to see. It is so easy to flare up with, 'But I only want my rights,' or to let fly in some other way. But if everyone kept doing that here, we'd be in a continual furor. When even one person is out of sorts, the whole place seems to pick up tension."

"Don't you think that women often get stirred up emotionally," I asked, "because they're afraid of what others are thinking about them or saying about them? I suppose that happens here."

"Yes, it does," answered Sue. "If you can put pride to one side and laugh at yourself and let other people laugh with you or even at you without feeling hurt, everyone comes out ahead. Too many things that a woman can be oversensitive about don't count much."

"It's in little ways that you have to watch your control," Sue went on. "I remember when I first came here I couldn't get used to some things. Then one day I caught myself at a silly trick. It must have been annoying to other guests. I would drum on the arm of my chair or on the table to keep my patience going. Just a monotonous little rhythm, enough to drive anyone else wild."

"Why, Sue!" exclaimed Mary. "You, of all people."

"Believe me," said Sue, "I kept catching myself at it for weeks."

"Did you stop it?" asked Harriet. "I haven't noticed any drumming business."

"Yes, and I'll tell you what cured me. It was seeing an irritating habit in another woman." Sue didn't look at Janet and she may have meant someone else, but what she said was, "This person marked time by sighing—a deep kind of sigh that was as dismal as a great discord."

Then she changed the turn of the subject by saying, "Self-control, of course, shows in conversation. One of the young Guild women the other day asked me how to keep others even-tempered while you talk with them, and I made several commonplace suggestions. Avoid contradicting. Avoid interrupting. Avoid correcting a detail that is being told in a story that you know. And don't try to better a story by capping it with one of your own that will outdo the first. These are old rules. And above all things, I advised, avoid overheated or even heated discussion. If a topic comes up that heads for disturbing argument, turn it off with a light touch."

"And speaking of a light touch," I said, "this is our seventh: Thou shalt dwell on the affirmative. Tell the girls, Sue, your method of dancing away from the negative."

"Oh, that's only one of my ways of meeting dark thinking or speaking," smiled Sue. "When something disagreeable tries to come into my head, I let my mind dance away with a quick step. Call it waltz away, if you like. What happens is that you find yourself dancing right into a pleasant or positive thought. It may be about the very same subject, too. Agreeable thinking doesn't depend on *what* you're thinking about but *how* you're thinking about it. It's the old story of facing the sun if you want your shadow to fall behind you."

"Now that so many experts are making a study of our minds and our souls," said Mary, "I notice one old proverb they all go back to: As a man 'thinketh in his heart, so is he.' "

"But, Sue," I said, "if you're going to shift your thinking quickly, you have to keep the switches of your train of thought—what shall I say?—everlastingly greased, don't you?"

"You're right," she answered, "you have to keep a light heart both to protect your imaginings about the future and to sift your memories of the past. If you're receptive to positive thoughts, surprising ideas may come into your head."

"I think memory control is sometimes very hard," I

said, "especially when you have a lot of time alone to think, as you do here."

"But memory can be a wonderful companion," Sue said, "in a home like this. Of course you have to use it wisely, not harping on unpleasant passages in your life that are long gone by, or on incidents that should be forgotten, or on times of personal sorrow. I always advise a woman to forget the date when her mother or husband or perhaps a young child died. At first she thinks I am heartless and mean her to be heartless. But no, some people nurse those anniversaries in continued grieving, when those are the very days for us to get outside ourselves and lift others.

"Fortunately," Sue went on, "there is for most women *people* a galaxy of happy dates and seasons in the year, crowded with lovely and loving reminders to be treasured. We can keep our minds centered on these recollections. Why, I can sit for an hour at a time and let my memory run over our marvelous life in the big Kentucky home."

"But doesn't that make you long too deeply for the good old days?" asked Harriet.

"If and when that feeling starts to come—and it does sometimes—I give my mind a little twist back to The Walden. For I know that I can live with the same spirit here in this room, if I will."

Mary was quick to pick this up to Sue's advantage.

"That," she said, "is exactly the way we feel about your entertaining us here, Sue," and she looked with a heartful of admiration into Sue's warm brown eyes. "It's you, not the room that makes all the difference to us, isn't it, girls?"

Sue passed over this and went back to the subject.

"I like to keep what I call a fair wind blowing through my mind," she said. "The remembrance of beauty once seen, thanksgiving for all the friendly worthwhileness of other days, the recollection of humorous touches and of serious achievement—these keep you true to the continual wonder and privilege of possessing a memory which, thank God, we five still have.

"I'm thinking, for instance," Sue went on, "about the simplest of out-of-door enjoyments. On reflection, how beautiful they can seem—all that has been good in sea and lake and river, in mountain and sky; bird on the wing and flower in the sun. All, too, that has been good and true in work and play and worship with family, friends, neighbors. A concert I remember with my favorite cellist or orchestra or soprano. A Dutch art exhibit, perhaps. Cathedrals I have seen and clergymen I have heard. Heights I have climbed. My life has been blessed with the generous, interesting, merry, affectionate, and uplifting." Sue poured this out eagerly and then asked us: "What more could you want?"

She didn't stop for an answer but hurried on. "From all this," she told us, "and by a quiet act of will, I can feed my soul in these later years with the enduring qualities of those earlier years. It's quite certain that one must forever be brushing away shadows that want to cling. But I have seen more than one elderly woman who knew how to hold the rounded ball of her life in both hands with a sure joy, as she turned it about. I can put my own finger this very minute on spots of my ball of remembrance that will glisten to the end. No one, nothing, can tarnish them; they are high and holy and only brighten with time."

We all sat very quietly and then Sue added, "Long ago the world was given an unlimited rule for thinking that has never been said more perfectly: 'Whatsoever things are true, whatsoever things are honorable, whatsoever things are just, whatsoever things are pure, whatsoever things are lovely, whatsoever things are of good report, think on these things.'"

Again we were still and then I said, "Perhaps it seems like a practical comedown, but our eighth topic is: Thou shalt keep occupied," and before Sue could say anything Harriet spoke with her usual vigor.

"Well, if you ask me, I'm fed up on these books and magazine articles that worry about adult occupation," she said. "We aren't children, any one of us here, and I hate this idea of being given busy-work."

"Just the same," came in Janet most unexpectedly, "I must say I wish I knew how to knit or do something or other. It would shorten the time and," here she hesitated, "and make me more like other people."

Only a short while ago, I thought, Janet was standing out for individuality. Perhaps one of those fair winds Sue had been talking about was blowing Janet's way.

"Can't you learn?" asked Harriet.

"I'm going to think about it," concluded Janet, and Sue took us on from there.

"It surely helps your morale," she said, "to produce concrete things that show, like a muffler that can be sent out on some mission. And this kind of work does bring us together in a friendly way. A few of our number are able to make a little money through their handiwork, the way your mother did," and Sue turned to me. "Yet some have to keep occupied in simple pursuits that aren't too productive. The Walden doctor said to us one day, 'When you're too tired for reading or sewing, you needn't feel out of things if you just sit quietly with a book or knitting in your lap, picking it up idly once every few minutes.' After all," Sue went on, "most of us here have earned a little out-and-out relaxation and laziness, without feeling apologetic. So long, of course, as we don't indulge in periods of harmful daydreaming, or of giving up, or of mulling over gloomy prospects.

"Many of us are able to make our own beds and do a little dusting in our rooms," Sue told us. "We have to admit that we take longer over dressing and small tasks than we used to, but it's good to know how to slow down and enjoy it. And there are many restful and diverting hobbies and amusements, if one is willing to take them up.

"In fact," she continued, "one way I make the acquaintance of a newcomer sometimes is to ask her to show me how to play a solitaire that I don't know. With all games here, by the way, it's wise to be a real sport in playing with other aging people—not to sulk like a child because of a 'poor hand.' Personally I don't care who wins so long as the loser is agreeable about it. The companionship is what counts."

"I suppose people here do read," said Harriet, "but what about actual study? I noticed a program posted on your bulletin board in the hall. I could go in for that sort of thing." *Bible study groups*

"Yes," answered Sue, "I'm often impressed by the variety of interests around here. Many just don't stop learning. They are really studying here. And the Guild members get us books when we want them. Recently The Walden received the bequest of a wonderful private library, small but with beautifully illustrated books of art, of travel, of history. When I saw the list, I felt as if our books from Kentucky were coming home to me here.

"Some," she went on, "can't see to read much, but they can borrow 'Talking Books' from the Library of Congress. I like to keep in touch with the changing world myself through the radio. And I often look in on a friend in the infirmary here who has to be propped against a staunch pile of bed pillows, because of her increasing weakness. But when politics begins to come into our conversation, as is bound to happen with her, she sits straight and unaided with her cheeks flushed and her opinions clear and incisive as ever. She really keeps me informed. One of her activities is to fold dressings for the Red Cross on the table that spans her bed, and when she gets excited about some political issue, she creases these with a bit of extra pressure.

"And there's a retired natural-science teacher out in the ell," Sue went on. "She led the local bird club here in town; you all may know her. For years she counted on her enjoyment of bird calls. Now that she's lost her hearing, she makes a hobby of feeding the birds at her window trays. I've often been summoned to her room with a hushing finger, to see a flock of chickadees and juncos, or the first-of-a-kind in the spring. Only yesterday she shared a letter from a friend in England about a pet bird.

"And that reminds me of another occupation here—a friendly one—the sharing of letters. I find myself running through my own mail over and over. Incoming letters and cards mean more here than you'd ever imagine. They 'take us places' and to people and events. You'll often see a knot of women around Mrs. Farnham when she gets the latest from her nine-year-old granddaughter. It's plain that the grandmother must write very humorous and understanding letters to Nina, whom we've all sort of adopted. Mrs. Farnham traveled widely in earlier years; and when she came here, she brought a collection of cards from all over the world. They start her off on stories; a card may show the quaint *pension* where she lived in France or a familiar masterpiece of art which she remembers seeing in some foreign gallery."

"Harriet," said Mary playfully, "used to be worried about being regimented into making aprons, Sue."

"I know what you mean, Harriet," Sue said, "but with your brain you're always going to find plenty to keep yourself occupied. As a matter of fact, when we use our abilities, even in moderation, we old girls sometimes uncover both physical and mental strength that is fun to possess. As someone points out, we're often tougher than you might think."

Then I went on, "The ninth topic reads: Thou shalt care about good grooming," and I looked at Sue.

"That's pretty clear as it stands," Sue said. "We can't all dress in the latest styles, but we can keep ourselves remarkably tidy and attractive, even so."

"Some don't," growled Janet. "You know well enough the two I mean—those sisters."

Sue brushed this aside with, "I was thinking especially of people who don't see too well any more, yet manage to stay presentable. I saw someone the other day helping to remove spots from the front of another woman's blouse. Most of us here care about how we look ourselves and how others look. Take that new guest in the room next to you, Janet. Her clothes may seem worn but she has won respect because she stands so straight."

"That's because she wears a girdle," put in Janet and one glance at her showed why she made this remark.

"It isn't easy to make suggestions to other people," Sue went on. "You can't very well tell a woman outright that her breath is unpleasant."

"Even if she knows it," objected Janet, "there isn't much she can do but let the rest of us stand it."

I wasn't surprised to have Sue come back with a practical answer to this.

"Oh, yes, there is," she said, "she can use one of those things with chlorophyll or something. I've known that to make a lot of difference."

I looked at Sue and said, "Here I find our last heading; Thou shalt show grace and good disposition. That seemed the best way to sum up what you and I talked about the other day."

"In a way it does cover everything else," said Sue, "and I like those words just for themselves. I'll tell you girls what they make me think of. In the corridor of a Southern hospital I once talked with an attendant who was caring for a friend of mine through an unusually trying illness. This motherly soul stood in her blue uniform ready to do anything possible to relieve the suffering. Nodding toward the patient's room, she said, 'Some people's characteristics jes' tramples on me right he-ah!' You know what she meant. A brave woman shows us that life isn't pleasant because of the place she is in, but life is made pleasant by her because she is in that place."

"It's really how gracious you can be, no matter what," I put in. "For my part it always seems to take character even to be pushed around in a wheelchair. That is, if you like feeling independent."

"I think this word *grace* includes thousands of little gestures," said Sue, "as little as these: Can I be one who passes the cream in a way to hide the shakiness of my neighbor's hands? Can I speak clearly to override the hearing difficulty of the woman across the table, in the cross current of voices that bothers her? Can I turn contentious talk into a more genial flow of conversation? Can I be the one who chooses to speak of things that have gone 'dead right'—not 'dead wrong'—or who helps the woman with failing sight but without seeming to notice that she is groping? How big—and I am forever wondering this for myself—how big, how outgiving can my mind and heart be? That is grace for you."

"And good disposition isn't just good humor," put in Mary. "I like to think it is being well-disposed toward life, toward the circumstances and the people that make up your life, as you find them. If you are able to keep your imagination and enthusiasm alive, you can fit in anywhere."

"Yes, grace and good disposition are mellow things, appreciated by everyone," concluded Sue, but Harriet met her with a great sigh.

"If you want to know what all this makes me feel like,"

she said, "I'll tell you. A large chunk of uncut marble that I'm barely beginning to chisel into what I want to be—into what I ought to be."

"Don't expect to carve your way out overnight," Mary suggested, and I said, "I warned you this would be a stiff session. It is personal stuff that hits right home, but I'm glad we've gone through it . . . together."

"I am, too," said Sue. She didn't look at Janet but added, "I think it has done Janet and me good. And so I'd like to share with you one of my favorite sentences from the *Letters of Direction,* by the Abbé de Tourville."

She opened a little book and read, " 'We learn much from the natural maturity which age brings to the spirit, provided'—notice that word *provided*—'that the spirit has already some depth of experience to which it spontaneously returns, and from which it draws quite different things from those which it drew before.'

"To me," Sue went on, "that reads like this. Every woman wears a mantle of experience, whether she wants to or not. This mantle is not what life has made of her but what she has made of life. As certain faculties fade, you might suppose that the mantle would get threadbare, lose color. But, if your mantle is woven of sturdy, dependable stuff, it wears well and somehow grows more becoming as you allow it to. If you get it soiled now and then by meager thinking or some ungracious act, you may have to wash it with strong discipline. Yet," and here Sue's eyes began to twinkle, as she relieved our tension, "yet if it's worth what it should be, you can freshen it easily and then just let it 'drip dry.' "

CHAPTER 13

Just Listen!

For days the beauty of the weather had invited every-one into the open and we three decided to take Sue and Janet for a picnic to a nearby lake.

"The food and everything will be different for them," I urged, and Harriet said she knew Eileen would make some of her jelly doughnuts.

"I think Eileen would do anything for us girls now," Harriet explained.

Mary arranged for Sue and me to ride in the back seat of her car and stowed Harriet and Janet in the front seat, stiff joints, canes, and all. We drove the long way and all talked at once about this reminiscence and that, as we passed familiar spots.

When we got out at the lakeside, Janet said, "To think that I used to snap the whip on the ice . . . right here!"

I thought she seemed to step with a little of the re-membered ease as she pointed one cane toward the water.

"And don't say I didn't!" she warned, starting us off in a merry spirit that we would hardly have expected of Janet a few weeks before.

When Mary and I had stretched out her red-and-white plaid cloth, we set up three folding chairs, but Sue would have none of them. As she settled down on the grass, she said something that ought not to have surprised me—not from her, that is. But to tell the truth, I don't remember ever picnicking with a small group when grace was asked.

Sue Reinhardt said, "Why don't we have an out-of-doors kind of blessing? Let's say the Twenty-Third Psalm together."

And we did. It may have been my imagination but I thought that Janet and perhaps Harriet faltered a bit fearfully over the words, "the valley of the shadow of death." In fact, Sue seemed to be the only one of us who didn't modify her voice. As I think of it now, I know that this was a sort of promise of what she was to tell us in her room a few days later. No doubt she took notice then of this faltering on our part and thought over what she could say to us, if the opportunity ever came. Sue never forced an opening to talk about anything. All along we had been the ones to prod her, and she had been the one to help our fears turn toward quiet determination and hope.

Now she put on her gay mood, however, and I wish I could recall some of the funny remarks she made. Somehow all the rest has stayed in my mind more clearly, but this was a side of Sue that we hadn't been seeing and I blessed Mary for thinking of having a picnic. Even Janet played back, and we all became good-naturedly relaxed.

It was for this that I must have been waiting. Finally

we came to that quiet moment when everything had been packed away in the baskets and the grass before us was tidy once more. If we had been five little children again, I'm sure we would have curled up then and there to have five naps. But as we sat looking across the calm of the lake, I took a small roll of paper from my knitting bag.

"You remember the other day," I said, "we brought up the question of the kind of restlessness that makes you want to escape from your environment—perhaps even from the rest home where you are living? I began thinking about this at home and, as usual, I had to sit down at my typewriter and write something out. It is fairly intimate," I apologized, "but I'm not afraid to read it to you girls. I thought it might fit best out of doors, and you will see why."

I paused a bit self-consciously, but when I looked at Sue I knew that something made me want to share this. She and Mary had been so generous with their most private thinking that I had worked over these pages with a willingness to let myself out to them.

"Everybody ready?" I asked. "Then here it is. I call it 'Just Listen!' "

As I went ahead I was aware that these friends knew it wasn't easy for me to read this to them, that they knew it came from pretty deep down somewhere, and I loved them for that. Even with the first word, they made me feel at ease. And this was it.

JUST LISTEN!

One of my deepest experiences came when Emma, my running mate of many years, died some four

years ago. Perhaps you know how it feels to have
loneliness suddenly walk in to be your companion.
If so, then you know the pang of trying to settle
down in the early evening when the other one is
no longer there, or the sharp sting of a solitary
Saturday afternoon, when everyone in your world
has gone somewhere with a special someone, the
way you two used to go. During the day you keep
busy but, as dark falls, it is as though you were always looking for something that never comes.

Soon after my loss, I was fortunate enough to
have invitations to visit three friends, one on a
little farm, one in a city apartment house, and one
on her lovely Pennsylvania estate. And, though I
didn't guess it at the time, the Holy Spirit was to
come as a comforter to me not in the shape of the
Biblical dove, but of a wood thrush—a series of
wood thrushes. I still believe they were God's way
of showing me that, as Jesus promised, He did not
leave us comfortless.

It is true that there is nothing strange about
finding a thrush. If you go where they like to be,
you are sure to see or at least hear them. But what
struck me was that the wood thrushes seemed to be
finding *me* during those next weeks, and in widely
differing places. First, there was the New Jersey
farmhouse. Helen and her husband went out to a
church-choir evening. I chose to stay at home with
the comfortable collie, Buffie. We two went out
to the stillness of the front porch, close to the farm

road. It was the first time I had really stopped to think—really think—since my friend had died.

Everything lay serene in the early mist that was starting in the low valleys, as serene as Buffie, stretched out with his nose between his front paws. Suddenly came a clear song from the tangled woods nearby.

"Just listen! A wood thrush!" I exclaimed.

Buffie listened. And I remembered.

As I look back now, I think something was happening to me in a small way like the promise in the Book of Acts: "Ye shall receive power, when the Holy Spirit is come upon you." It was as though I was beginning to receive new power to relieve my tiredness and my uncertainty as to how to go ahead with life. . . .

My next hostess had a city apartment facing a blank brick wall. But one end of the living room did give a glimpse up into three tall elms. At dusk, while we sat renewing old ties, a clear song came to us from outside the window.

"Just listen, Anne," I said with surprise, "there's a wood thrush right here in the city."

And Anne said, without surprise, "Why, yes!"

I must have put this into my memory very securely. Perhaps the Holy Spirit was beginning to teach me. But I was still slow about learning. I knew that.

My next refuge was a large estate in Lancaster County, Pennsylvania, with wide spaces within as well as without my friend Agnes's home. She had recently lost her husband and knew what it was to be alone. As I was dressing for dinner in my cool green room, and quite as though I had expected it, yes, out in the great oak by my open window sat a wood thrush, singing and singing.

I wish that at the time I might have had right at hand the verse from the Gospel of St. John which I have been thinking about since then: "And I will pray the Father, and He shall give you another Comforter, that He may be with you forever, even the Spirit of truth. . . . Ye know Him, for He abideth with you and shall be in you." Glancing back now, I think I was only dimly aware of the presence of the Holy Spirit and certainly not of His abiding in me. I gave my feeling no name, even though I was then on the very edge of a definite experience.

At the dinner table I remember saying to Agnes simply this: "It's a funny thing. The wood thrush has chased me on my whole tour. He seems to be everywhere. I shall hate to leave his music— and personality—behind."

But in time I did return to my apartment, close to the noise of a busy town square. That first night I went to sleep with a mind roaming securely through recent memories, glad that the familiar church spire was nearby. Yet I wasn't really at home yet, not in my heart. I wasn't going to face reality till the next day.

When morning came, I might have been any-

where. Before I had time to know that I was alone,
right there on my own street I heard something.
And this time I didn't say, "There's a wood thrush."
In my delight I said aloud, "Just listen! *Here's* a
wood thrush!"

My thoughts went back to my three hostesses,
to how we had talked of God and faith and suffering and hope, as people sometimes will. I knew
that I had gone away from my home in despair
and loneliness, but now I was assured of a very
personal and divine love surrounding me—assured
through this sign. Christ had promised, "But the
Comforter, even the Holy Spirit, whom the Father
will send in my name, He shall teach you all things
and bring to your remembrance all that I said unto
you."

I now believe that the Holy Spirit had been
teaching me, had been bringing the intent of
Christ's life and death to my remembrance. My
assurance had come through this symbol of peace,
of comfort, and of joy. And now, as I woke to my
first morning alone again, I found that I was not
alone.

I remember having a verse from the Old Tes-
tament come to my mind, the words that Jacob
exclaimed when he awoke from his dream: "Surely
the Lord is in this place, and I knew it not." As my
eyes glanced about at accustomed objects a new
version came to me, like an echo, clear and certain:
"Surely the Lord is in this place—and *I know it!*"

Something told me that God never goes away,

even when I try to escape Him and His loving care. And there was a new lightness in my heart.

I hesitated to look up, for the girls seemed very quiet there by the lake. But after a pause, I said, "Goodness! I hope that doesn't sound too smug."

Mary looked at me out of her understanding and said, "You know very well it doesn't. That was written with the heart."

"Thanks for thinking so, Mary," I said. "It really did happen, just like that . . . the series of thrushes, I mean."

The woods along the shore made no stir in the stillness of high noon. Sue glanced around at all of us and then rested her eyes on Janet.

"Perhaps," she said, "we've missed a thrush at The Walden, by coming out here today!"

CHAPTER 14

"*Millions of Surprises*"

A few days passed before we were once again in Sue's room, and we seemed to have a more close and natural togetherness than we had had at any time before. It was the picnic that did it, I thought to myself. Before sitting down, I took up from the table a recent book on thought-control.

"Is this good, Sue?" I asked.

"Yes, I think so," she answered. "My friends from the Guild bring me things from the library along this line because I like to keep up with what's coming out. I find there's something especially worth practicing in each one of them."

Now Sue hesitated as though she had something she wanted to talk about, very much.

"But you'll remember," she went on, "that some time ago I spoke of the Bible as the real reference book for the rest home. I began giving a lot more thought to that the other day, after I came across three lines from a poem by

George Herbert." Sue turned to the flyleaf of her Bible and read to us what she had written there:

"Bibles laid open, millions of surprises,
 Blessings beforehand, ties of gratefulness,
 The sound of glory ringing in our ears.

"Today's search for security and peace," Sue continued, "isn't new. Isaiah and St. Paul recognized the very feelings that frustrate us now. They saw the human need of a quiet soul because of what they themselves went through. The men who contributed to our best seller were not only often inspired but always experienced as well. Their words of power, of joy, of confidence, of hope have had reason to stand up under wear. Reading them today gives you a sense of the dignity and importance of your own life, regardless of your years.

"Sometimes," Sue told us, "I learn a verse from the American Revised Version, which I happen to know best, and sometimes from the King James Version for its pure beauty. For some passages I combine the versions in a way to bring me the most meaning. I enjoy, too, the clear expression of many verses in the more recent translations, especially the Revised Standard Version. I like whatever phrasing is the simplest, the most easy to understand and live by. Take these bits," Sue said, slipping a sheet of paper from the front of her Bible:

"Lo, I am with you always.
 Abide in me and I in you. . . . Abide ye in my love.
 In quietness and in confidence shall be your strength.

Rest in the Lord.

God is our refuge and strength, a very present help. . . .

He shall cover thee with His feathers and under His
wings shalt thou trust.

The eternal God is thy dwelling-place and underneath
are the everlasting arms.

Lead me to the Rock that is higher than I.

Through God we shall do valiantly.

Peace I leave with you; my peace I give unto you.

Be still and know that I am God.

Just think of it. After all that has been written through the
intervening years, there remains for us this one supreme
reference book on peace and health."

Here Harriet broke in like her old self, but I knew that
she spoke for all three of us who were still living out in the
free world.

"Sue," she said, "no matter how many books I read I'm
still afraid of the change I know has to come."

"That's only normal, Harriet," Sue said with a friendly
shrug of the shoulders. "Don't be afraid of saying so. It's
much better than to put on a bold front to try to deceive
yourself and others. Such a change is a change. That is why
feeling the presence of God is so necessary, because He
doesn't change. I remember at the start of living here I used
lines from a certain hymn, over and over:

> In heavenly love abiding,
>   No change my heart shall fear;
> And safe is such confiding,
>   For nothing changes here."

We had all seated ourselves long before this and Janet had motioned for Sue to take the easy chair that we usually left for Janet's comfort. It was almost as though she knew that this would be a special gathering and that Sue would be the center of it.

Sue glanced around the circle now with her brown eyes and went on, "This leads me to tell you about a Mrs. Raymond down the hall, whom I've come to know lately. Her mind seems thoroughly tired out, and I am told that she gave the best of herself to taking care of a sister until she herself had a sort of breakdown. She's a good deal older than we girls are. She has the most beautiful face, like a delicate miniature painted on warm ivory. At present she finds it hard to concentrate, but I have discovered something I want to share with you."

I noticed that Sue turned first to Mary, though she was speaking to all of us.

"At Miss Holden's suggestion one day soon after Mrs. Raymond came here," Sue said, "I dropped in on her. After sitting quietly with her for a while and then talking about next to nothing, I thought of the shepherd Psalm that we said together at the picnic the other day. And I said, 'I like the Psalm that begins, "The Lord is my shepherd, I shall not want. He maketh me to lie down in green pastures; He leadeth me beside the still waters. He restoreth my soul."'

"Then for the first time Mrs. Raymond spoke to me.

"She said, 'Yes, I do, too,' and a light of comfortable recognition had come into her eyes. So, as I sat thinking of this with her, one of my favorite hymns came to mind and I said, 'And I like the hymn that begins,

Love divine, all loves excelling,
Joy of heaven to earth come down.'

"Again she spoke, looking at me with those deepset eyes
that held the clear glow of longtime faith.

" 'Yes, I like it, too,' she said, slipping her worn hand
into mine, there on her lap.

"We seemed to have come together on holy ground,"
Sue explained to us, "where her weakness could be steadied
with a familiar strength. I fastened my eyes on her and I
thought, but without speaking out loud, 'Surely, the love
and the peace and the joy of God are in you.' It was as
though she heard me, for she drew my hand more closely
into hers and said, 'Thank you.' "

As Sue paused, I couldn't help looking at Janet, and it
was plain that she hadn't known of this before. I had never
seen her so transfixed. She sat gazing at Sue as though she
couldn't really take this in. None of us spoke and Sue seemed
eager to go on. An amused expression flashed across her
face as she began:

"You know how, when you want to give refreshment to
a guest who comes unexpectedly into your home, you go to
a special stock. In that cupboard you find some of your company jelly and other things you hardly remembered you had
on hand. Well, I suddenly realized that in my Bible there
were those 'millions of surprises' that I could choose from
to give to Mrs. Raymond. I knew that my spiritual Corner
Cupboard wasn't bare. For years I had been laying in my
favorite foods by way of verses, hymns, and prayers, and I
was very glad now.

"So I came back to my room that first day and gradually assembled several groups of verses from the Psalms and other parts of the Bible, like those I told you I used for sleep. And from my hymn book I took choice lines. It was my guess that many of them would be well-known to my new friend. Then I was able to get Miss Simmons, the volunteer secretary here at The Walden who sometimes comes in to visit with me, to type them all out.

"Now I go in to see Mrs. Raymond and we enjoy these together. I have felt sure from the little extra grasp she gives to my hand from time to time that these are familiar to her, that she brought them here in that head and heart of hers. This morning she even said the whole of the Lord's Prayer with me. It's as though we had always known each other, as though we were talking over old days."

Sue waited to let each of us draw conclusions for herself. But I believe she couldn't tell from our faces whether we saw her point. So she came to our aid in her own way.

"Have you ever watched the ebbing of the tide? I mean through those moments of wavering before the turn. The waves have weakened. They seem almost to sigh with a sense of nothingness. Then the pickup begins. But there is a sag and yet another sag. Now some dependable magnet gives force to the turn and floodtide truly begins. The power that draws the sea back and forth in its eternal surge has been there all the while."

Sue paused again and I knew that she was not seeing us but, in her mind's eye, was picturing her special friend.

"This is what seemed surely to be happening with Mrs. Raymond," she explained, and with no doubt in her voice. "As we read together, I felt a new pulsing of strength in her hand and I saw in her eyes an increasing response like the first quiet lapping of returning tide. A Power that she had long known was at work."

I turned and looked at Janet, as I often did when perhaps I should have been searching my own soul. There seemed a new understanding in her whole bearing, a new eagerness that did me good. Sue broke the spell by reaching for a folder on the lower shelf of her table.

"These," she told us, "are carbon copies that Miss Simmons made. I thought you all might like them to go over now and then, so that we can be enjoying them together. Just for use among us I had the first page headed: *Sue Reinhardt's Corner Cupboard*. And under the heading is one of my favorites: 'Your joy no one taketh away from you.'

"Verses from the Bible can be like familiar tunes that stay in your head. You hum them; they even hum themselves. You have them there on call, as a continual source of power, or to help you meet some sudden challenge to your poise. At such times the steadying assurance of just one familiar line may flood your mind like sunlight flooding a room."

Here Sue brought herself up with a start.

"How I'm running on," she chuckled, "like an old lady, as they say! But seriously," she explained, separating the copies that lay in her lap, "I think if you take these with you —and I really mean this—it may strengthen Mrs. Raymond to have us all reading and trusting the same words that she and I will be using together here."

Mary stepped swiftly to Sue's side and took the papers. As she distributed them, I was aware of a spiritual knitting of us five into a group. I hadn't thought of us quite like that before. And, instead of looking to see how Janet or Harriet accepted this plan, I found that I was watching myself. I believed, without knowing it, I must have prayed then and there to be worthy of Sue's rich friendship, to be able to contribute all I ought to this atmosphere of sharing. Now she was telling us a little more.

"I asked Miss Simmons," she said, "to type the poet's name and date with each hymn, especially the date. It's always arresting to me to think about those dates. My own anxieties somehow fall into perspective when I know that a man in 1755, over two centuries ago, found security in taking the 'anxious load' that pressed down his 'weary mind' to the Heavenly Father to find 'sweet refreshment,' as it is worded."

Sue looked over her copy of the verses and hymns and then remarked, "You may wonder why I included a full reference to the Christmas story from the early chapters of the Gospel according to St. Luke. That is what I keep re-reading with Mrs. Raymond, and it has given me a surprising enjoyment at this season of the year. Here in this part of the country people associate Christmas with snow. The first time it came into my head to read the Nativity story to Mrs. Raymond (because of its certain familiarity to her), I felt as though I were doing something out of place. It was one of the hottest days we've had. Yet this brought home to me with fresh wonder the real timelessness—or shall I say also, the real placelessness—of the birth of Christ. It was an event for all time, all places, all people. And Mrs. Raymond and I are two of these people. So I even asked Miss Simmons to include one of the Christmas hymns here, my favorite of them all, I suppose, and perhaps yours, too:

[*161*]

O little town of Bethlehem,
How still we see thee lie!"

We fingered over our copies and then Mary said, "I see
some of my special Bible verses here, Sue:

Thou hast put gladness in my heart.
Thou, O Lord, art a shield about me;
    my glory and the lifter up of my head.

"When a dark or unpleasant thought pushes into my
mind, I try to flash verses like these on it, and then it has to
leave. I don't think," Mary went on slowly, "the same verse
always helps me in the same kind of need. But they are all
meant for 'enlightening the eyes.' That must be why I sometimes think of the ecstasy a child feels at watching fireflies
or glowworms that are glancing now here, now there. The
Bible seems filled with fireflies—verses that give off a sudden glow, if you look carefully."

Sue started to speak, hesitated, and then said, "I think
I'll tell you girls something rather intimate. It may sound
rather strange to you, especially if you've never belonged to
a prayer group. But I did belong to one in our church in
Kentucky. And I keep my membership in it and they all
know this. That means that every day at a particular hour
I am with them in the spirit of prayer, and they tell me it
helps them to be aware of this. It helps me, I'm sure. But
that's the way prayer is," she added. "I pray for the minister,
for the church organizations and officers, and for those of the
parish who may be troubled in body, mind, or spirit, even
though I do not know their names as I used to. And I ask

God to give them all down there the fullness of His joy each day. I know that some people think of prayer groups with raised eyebrows, as an 'escape.' Very good. They are. But it is an escape with friendly spirits out into the open, into the freedom of God's far-flung Presence. And I am glad of the way the usefulness of such groups is spreading all over the world."

No one made a comment. Sue had given us something quite outside ourselves to think about. I remember that it was new to me to think that, in such a place as The Walden, away from familiar environment and people, one could pray out into all the needy reaches of the earth, both giving and receiving at the same time.

"That's wonderful," I finally said; then I turned to Sue. "You spoke of praying with Mrs. Raymond," I went on, "but Sue, I don't really know how to pray, not regularly and well, I think."

"There are many helpful little books of prayers and about praying which can be used easily," Sue answered me. "I keep several at hand and go from one to another according to my need. Often I find myself saying the brief prayer that an elderly friend of mine uses to steady her endurance. It is really a sort of affirmation-prayer: 'God is helping me now.' This is simple, but simple ways are often the most profound," said Sue, and I saw Harriet nod her head in approval.

"At The Walden I have found an unexpected amount of time free for prayer," Sue went on. "You can always talk to God and listen to Him. That is one of the many freedoms here. And it is good to learn how to push the windows of prayer open. I think that God must enjoy using some of our leisure to channel His good through our prayers to those who are busied with active life and to people in need any-where.

"So long as we care about the welfare of everyone on His earth, we can pray for all worthy movements, for peace and good will among all men. Who knows, it may be your prayer or mine that will tip the scales for world peace? And as we look above our own petty concerns that might other-wise close us in, we breathe a higher air. We need largeness of soul and firm beliefs to roam around in when we spend most of our time within one room. Prayer is a powerful realm, and moving around in it gives a sense of space and of well-being to the one who prays."

As often with us nowadays, no one spoke for several minutes.

Then I said, "I think you're marvelous to do all this for us—and for your neighbor."

Sue turned with a quick start of denial.

"No," she said firmly, "you don't quite understand. What pours into me from these moments with Mrs. Ray-mond forms the best proof I have ever experienced of the promise of Jesus, 'Where two or three are gathered together in my name, there am I in the midst of them.' It takes only two to intensify the sense of His responsive presence."

"And think of it," Mary said with deliberation, "right here there are five of us."

CHAPTER 15

The Twilight of It All

The day we asked Sue Reinhardt to name for our next visit drew into a beautiful evening. Always before this we had gone to The Walden in the daytime, but Sue told us that they had an early supper and it was our guess that sometimes the evenings seemed lonely. As things turned out, it proved just right that we should be there through a lovely long twilight.

On the way over with Mary and Harriet I brought up a topic that wasn't particularly full of sunshine.

"I'm afraid," I confessed, "that, in spite of everything, I still dread living with other aging people and watching their vigor and faculties fail, especially the ability to think clearly."

Instantly I recognized that this might carry Mary's mind back to the months when she had watched the waning of her husband's life. That, it seemed to me, must have been a private, a very personal torture, at a time when no doctor

could give him further relief. I had been told that she had
seen John again and again when he was too confused to
recognize her, and only those who have waited in that cir-
cumstance know what it takes from the loving watcher. But
Mary didn't shrink at my reminder.

"From my own experience, I find only one answer—the
very answer Sue has given us," she told me, "a serene awareness of the presence of God. This awareness can hold up a
curtain that hides what you don't need to see, what you
can't do anything about. You know the kind of glass that is
used for ultramodern schoolrooms. Parents and visitors can
look through this glass as through a one-way screen.

"I used to feel," she went on, "that John could always
see me, clearly, but something protected me from anything
distressing in his appearance, or even his mental confusion.
As long as I could keep him in our home, before he was
hospitalized, I began every morning with some Bible verse
for my own use, like those Sue has talked with us about. 'I
can do all things in Him that strengtheneth me' was one of
my most reliable screens. Somehow this practice enabled me
to see John's face increasingly affected by his malady without cringing—to sit across the table from him and simply
see the man I loved behind that face. . . . Not that I became callous. My heart became only the more sensitive, yet
I had strength given me that canceled out the hurt. I can't
explain how it was that I cared greatly about his suffering,
yet it seldom overwhelmed me."

Mary had been driving slowly as she talked. Harriet
and I didn't speak all the rest of the way to The Walden.
And when we went in, it was as though Sue had known what
we were just saying because she didn't wait for idle pleasant-

ries. As soon as Janet and the rest of us were seated, she took up the thread.

"Do you know, girls," Sue said, "I've often thought over the chat we had that day about surmounting the suffering of others. I do believe that God can protect us even when the angel of death comes here. When your reason tells you that the natural course for the body forbids cure of another woman—that her way obviously lies due west, this is not a contradiction of your belief that 'with God all things are possible.' You know that it is now 'possible' for Him to shepherd that person in His own wisdom through the finale. However it may look, I believe that in His wisdom this can be with each one truly a grand finale for 'He knows the way He taketh.'

"It wasn't until I came here and had been here some time that I caught the flash of a new meaning in the verse, 'I will fear no evil, for Thou art with me.' I had never before stressed the word *no.* I had given half-trust only, allowing myself to fear *some* evil—not being willing to let go completely. Then, too, I worked on that word *for;* it leads me to the reason why I can commit my mind to fearing *no evil whatsoever—because* He is with me, yes, with *me.*"

Everyone sat without stirring, as though we were literally at Sue's feet, and she continued slowly.

"In a place like this," she said, "it should be possible, though not easy, to see a dying neighbor as in God's hands, to know that in His sight she has continued wholeness."

Sue leaned back in her chair and smiled thoughtfully, as though she didn't want to keep us in too great tension.

Then she said, "I think I didn't mention that other day the great relief you can find if you *do* something for such a neighbor. And I mean little things. Send in to her a share of your flowers, even when she may not be able to take in that they have come from you. A rose is never dumb. And, if her eyes can no longer enjoy the color, the scent may speak comfort to her beyond thinking.

"You remember," Sue went on, "that I spoke of 'millions of surprises' to be found in the Bible. I have one that never fails to quiet me. It fortifies my mind in the midst of otherwise confusing sights and sounds:

> In the multitude of my thoughts within me
> Thy comforts delight my soul."

Harriet moved restlessly and I said to myself, "She's only partially satisfied. Something in her still begs for an answer."

Sue must have noticed this, too, for she gave Harriet a look of encouragement.

"I hate to put it into words, with you two living here," Harriet hesitated, "yet in many ways we three have already joined you. It's this. Sometimes when I come into The Walden they just all seem . . . seem to be . . . *waiting.*"

I glanced quickly at Sue and saw her ready herself with an alert motion of the head as if she had wished for this opening. Perhaps, I thought, she wants this for Janet as well as for the rest of us.

"You mean waiting to die, Harriet? Then don't be afraid of the word *death*," Sue said with assurance. "It is such an individual thing. I have felt that over and over when I have been with those who neared the end. It is so individual that you have only to be natural in meeting it—for yourself or for others. The mistake is to try to steel yourself against that time.

"For each of us," she went on, "the ministering angel will come to close the final page of life. But how, when, where, we do not know. From observation I believe that whatever tranquillity I may have practiced before will make the passage easier. This will be the time when my experience in placing my hand trustfully into the hand of the Father in hours of need will pay out, because I shall find use for a trust that has been tried—a strong and quiet trust."

Mary murmured assent to this and I felt the eagerness with which all four of us were watching Sue.

"Of course there's always," she said, "a good chance that you will be in possession of your faculties and conscious enough so that your last hours can be your final testimony of service. You look puzzled, Harriet, and you, too, Janet. I'll tell you what I mean. You remember our talk about being of help to the members of the personnel in a home. What a marvel it would be if a person had so cultivated the art of appreciation that, even in her last weakness, a word of thanks or some motion that speaks thanks, came of its own easy accord. Without seeming effort, which one might not be able to exert anyway, an unselfish something might fill the very air."

"If you could do that," I remarked slowly, "no matter how your physical powers were waning, you wouldn't be called 'helpless.' You'd be helping your helpers . . . and helping yourself."

"I almost suppose," admitted Harriet, "that I really like talking about death out in the open."

A rare rose glow from the sunset was streaming into

Sue's room, lighting the faces there, softening the intentness, tempering the tension. The light struck the mirror and glanced over to the white dress Janet was wearing, illumining her face with a light I had never imagined there. Or was her very face changed, I wondered as Harriet went on.

"I guess, Sue," she confessed, bending forward, "the trouble with me is that I don't know just what immortality is going to be like."

"But nobody knows, Harriet," interrupted Mary.

"Whenever I start to think the thing through," Harriet explained, looking from Mary to Sue, "I start . . . *period*. What's the matter with me?"

"The same thing that's the matter with most of us," replied Sue. "We confuse knowing with believing and think they must be one and the same. We've become so dependent on the word 'laboratory-tested' that we let the idea hold us back from believing what we can't see proven with our own eyes.

"We use the phrase 'doubting Thomas' rather casually," she continued, "but what happened to him is what we'd like to have happen to us. He wanted to be shown and Jesus understood this. Thomas wouldn't believe what the other disciples told him, that they had seen the resurrected Lord. Thomas said, 'Except I shall see in His hands the print of the nails, and put my finger into the print of the nails, and put my hand into His side, I will not believe.'

"And what took place?" asked Sue, making a wide but confident gesture with her hands. "The risen Christ came and stood in the midst of His disciples some days later and what did He do first? He said, 'Peace be unto you.' I think He meant this especially to remind Thomas that he must quiet his doubts and open his mind to the truth he couldn't bring himself to take in. I have often thought there must have been a holy pause of silence after that blessing, which was a command as well.

"Then we see," she went on, "how Jesus understood this common human frailty that you are so anxious to overcome, Harriet. He said to Thomas, 'Reach hither thy finger, and see my hands; and reach hither thy hand, and put it into my side.' He let Thomas not only see but actually feel, to reinforce his belief. Jesus then gave the clear directive, 'Be not faithless, but believing.' "

Sue stopped here, but Harriet pressed her with, "So what? For us, that is? For me?"

We all waited for the answer. In even Janet's eyes there was a look of expectation that was somehow free of doubt.

Then Sue said, "You've been a teacher, Harriet. You know the role of demonstration. Jesus was the greatest of all teachers, and at this hour, when He could have gone forth to impress the masses, He did what any patient teacher will do. He took time with His backward pupil, Thomas. By means of perhaps the most graphic demonstration in the whole history of pedagogy, He explained that what had happened had happened.

"Just think, girls," she went on and it did seem that we were none other than Sue's pupils at the moment, "just think what it must have meant to that Great Teacher when Thomas came out with the answer to his own question, 'My Lord and my God!' This was a wonderful declaration of faith, but did Jesus leave it at that? No, He went on to give Thomas the far-reaching answer that we need today, to steady ourselves for an undated tomorrow.

" 'Because thou hast seen me,' He said, 'thou hast believed; blessed are they that have not seen, and yet have believed.' "

"You think, then, Sue," I said, "that the hesitation of Thomas about the resurrection of Jesus is in spirit like our hesitation about our own afterlife?"

Sue put one hand quietly in the other on her lap.

"You can even assume," she said, "that Christ was thinking of this as a proof to Thomas that he, too, would never really die. Only a few days before, at the Last Supper, Jesus must have looked around that table at the eleven faithful as at eleven personal and quite individual friends, when He assured them comfortably, 'I go to prepare a place for you.' I think He meant very definitely a spiritual place for each one of them, His beloved disciples."

"You mean," Harriet came in, "that this is for each of us personally, if we can ever persuade ourselves?"

She looked a bit plaintively at Sue, yet her face was full of a rather lovely wonder, as she turned to the rest of us.

"Please don't think I'm a pagan," she said, "but Sue seems to have thought this thing through. I guess I've been avoiding that."

"No, Harriet, it's too much to say that I've thought it through," said Sue positively. "That's just what you can't do. It isn't thinking; it goes far beyond mere thinking, to believing. As that verse phrases it, 'Blessed are they that have not seen, and yet have believed.' You know Pascal said, 'The heart has its reasons which reason knows nothing of.' "

Sue reached out for her Bible and opened to verses she told us were in the second chapter of First Corinthians.

"Paul understood this pretty well," she said, "when he

referred back to the Book of Isaiah: 'But as it is written, Eye hath not seen, nor ear heard, neither have entered into the heart of man the things which God hath prepared for them that love Him. But God hath revealed them unto us by His Spirit; for the Spirit searcheth all things, yea, the deep things of God.' "

Sue stopped reading and placed the Bible again on the table beside her.

"I think what Harriet is saying, Sue," I put in, "is that you've done a lot more thinking than we have and with a lot more believing. *Your* spirit has been searching all things, 'the deep things of God.' I must confess that I've been accepting some of these assurances like so many words and haven't pushed beyond them to a meaning for my own belief. Mary," I went on, "you've kept still about most of this. I'm sure you have a clear-cut faith about death."

"If I have, it's no credit to me," Mary answered. "When you walk beside the person dearest to you through his last long illness, as it is called, you have plenty of time to come to strong conclusions. What I was really doing, or that's the way it seemed to me then, was to reach up eagerly for the things that matter, so that I might give John assurance to rest on. We never talked about death, John and I, but he had always been clever about knowing what I was thinking —it was a sort of joke with us—and I am sure that my increasing faith in immortality must have done something for him, because it did something for me that has truly lasted."

Mary, it appeared, was giving us a sort of bequest out of all that she had had to go through. And, if ever I felt the presence of an unknown person, at that moment I could have said that her John was there, ready himself to lift our faith to an "assurance of things hoped for, a conviction of things not seen."

"Without belief," Mary added, "one can know a great loneliness, and it is in such loneliness that fear thrives."

We all paused to think and then I gave a sigh.

"Do you know," I said, "this whole thing has been simmering in me for a long time—this doubt and questioning, I mean. Now all I can say is that you two have *gentled* me. . . . And that is a wonderful gift."

Of course Mary and Sue waived this off, but I saw Harriet nodding her head in agreement.

"I think," I went on, "you have told me that I had faith of sorts. There's nothing you've said that I didn't already believe in a way. But you've done something to give me hope."

I could see that the tension lines in Harriet's forehead had gradually ironed out and I said, "Perhaps you've got to mix hope with faith, or what you believe doesn't mean anything; it's just words, words that you hear and say and like but don't actually lean on."

At this point, I remember noticing that Harriet was opposite the low mirror. Without her knowing it, I looked and looked at her face as Sue went on. There was a relaxation in it that did my heart good. Her eyes seemed to be a deeper blue in their new quietness.

On pretense of reaching to the dresser for my handbag, I caught a glimpse of my own face beside hers and a slow smile came over my features, like an answer to a query. For I knew this was not the face that I had been seeing in my hall mirror. I could see that I, too, had gained a sense of security and I said to myself, *"It's a wonderful feeling not to be frightened any more."*

And now Sue was talking again.

"Yes," she was saying, "I am not afraid of death because of that very mixture of faith and hope. I think that everyone has to find in her own heart her description of what resurrection means. This is an individual privilege, a part of our freedom. However vague our actual picture has to be in every detail, our trust can be certain with our own personal kind of certainty."

Then Mary took us on in her way.

"For myself," she said, "I don't find it difficult to believe that here and now I live and move and have my being in God. So my imagination finds it easy to rest in the surety that there will be for me a continuation of that very abiding-place, spiritually speaking. How different, how much more intimate, more glorious, that eternal 'house not made with hands' is to be, must remain a seeming mystery to me. But many seeming mysteries in my life so far have been solved and made as clear and bright as noonday. Sometimes I rather think I enjoy not knowing. Just awaiting a surprise. Just believing. Just trusting. As Whittier put it, 'I only know I cannot drift beyond His love and care.'"

"I have to admit," said Sue, "that the physical aspect of my leaving this world may prove to be ordinary in its nature. That isn't in my power to direct. But I'm not going to let the spiritual aspect crumble if I can help it."

At this point I looked at Janet and she seemed almost moved to say something to us, but she simply readjusted herself in her chair. Somehow I wanted to give her comfort. Perhaps, I thought, she isn't so far behind the rest of us after all.

So I said, "Of course it's silly to worry about unpleasant

things that may very well never happen. Aren't we told over and over that many people go quietly in their sleep?"

Janet gave me a quick glance of appreciation and I knew that I had hit my mark.

"That's very true," said Sue. Then, after a pause, "You have to combine a sort of calm reason with a sturdy faith when you look ahead to the end. And like many things we five have been talking over in recent weeks, facing it frankly robs it of false fear. Of course we'd like to slip away easily and without too great inconvenience to any who are attending to our needs.

"I must confess," she went on, "that I hope the candle of my mind may shine with clear light to the last. But if the flame should burn dimly or flicker strangely, I pray God to give an unearthly strength and wisdom to my caretakers in their uneasy task. Even now I can feel compassion for them, with gratitude to match. As one of us suggested a while ago, I only hope to have a thankful heart that there are people at that time—doctor, nurses, and others—who have the good will and the ability to look after me. As these attendants find me approaching the final rest, I would wish that somehow their endurance may be quickened by my own strong hope in God. It would be a wonderful last achievement on earth, wouldn't it?"

As Sue grew silent, I felt one of Harriet's objections coming.

"But all that takes a conscious sort of buoyancy, doesn't it?" she asked. "And you just don't have buoyancy when you're at that point."

She looked cautiously at Sue, almost afraid that she would produce an answer, and she did.

"What I can give you on that, Harriet," Sue said, "has to come from my own experience. It isn't anything I've read in some book. I think that you can cultivate a spiritual resilience that increases as your physical resilience declines. I mean, I suppose, a kind of counterbalance that stands by. After all, you are at that time approaching the moment of passing into a life of perfect balance. It seems only a gallant way to make the crossing in a sort of prepared and even receptive mood."

"Not, that is, with a reluctant or fearful growl," I put in, and Harriet smiled.

Then Mary spoke.

"After all, isn't this gallant approach found in the lives of many great men and women?" she asked. "I mean that they aren't heroic while in full vigor, only to turn coward at the end. Perhaps it is because, as the verse says, God 'hath set eternity in their heart.' Take Joan of Arc. Her purpose schooled her spiritual nature so that she not only stayed rational and calm at the stake, but was able to pray to the last. And they say that the name of Jesus was the final word she was heard to speak."

"That kind of praying," observed Sue, "always seems at once an outlet and an inlet."

I watched her hold those warm brown eyes on Janet as she spoke. It was as if Sue had been feeling all five of us within the active circle of the discussion there in the twilight. I saw Janet start to respond. She was really readying herself to give us something, though this plainly took effort of mind and of will. Sue, with her usual intuition, kept looking at Janet with a friendly, urgent smile.

Then Janet Coombs began. "I think," she said, "I might

tell you a story about a great-uncle of mine who lived to quite an age." She hesitated. "When the doctor declared that his life was closing, the minister was called in. It must have been the custom to sit by the bedside and quote solemn words from the Bible. So he started in a threatening voice, 'It is a fearful thing to fall into the hands of the living God.'

"They say," and a flicker of satisfaction crossed Janet's face, "they say that at this my uncle not only stirred but sat upright in his bed and inquired confidently, 'Who else's hands would you want to be falling into?' "

TRINITY
UNITED METHODIST CHURCH